Enid Blyton

FIVE MINUTE
TALES

Brer Rabbit suddenly tore down the hill into the gully clashing the tin plates with all his might, his tin mugs clattering behind him.

'Ho, ho, ho!' he yelled. 'Here I come, I'm the Spewter-Splutter Man, I'm snaggle-toothed and double-jointed, I've claws in my hands and scales down my back! Ho, ho, ho!'

Enid Blyton's
FIVE MINUTE
TALES

MAMMOTH

First published in 1933
by Methuen & Co Ltd
Published 1992 by Mammoth
an imprint of Mandarin Paperbacks
Michelin House, 81 Fulham Road, London SW3 6RB

Mandarin is an imprint of Reed Consumer Books Ltd

Copyright © Enid Blyton 1933

Enid Blyton is a registered trademark of Darrell Waters Ltd

ISBN 0 7497 1182 5

A CIP catalogue record for this title
is available from the British Library

Printed in Great Britain
by Cox & Wyman Ltd, Reading, Berkshire

CONTENTS

Brer Rabbit's House

ONCE upon a time Brer Rabbit and his friends thought they would build a fine big house, and live there all together.

So they began. Brer Bear carried the bricks, Brer Wolf set in the windows, Brer Fox fetched the doors, and Brer Terrapin walked about and got in everybody's way. Brer Rabbit stuck a pencil behind his ears, and went about measuring and marking, looking very busy, but doing no work at all.

Well, at last the house was finished, and all the animals moved in. Brer Rabbit chose a room upstairs, and a fine room it was too.

Now the first evening all the animals talked together in the parlour, but after a while Brer Rabbit got up and said he guessed he would go up to his room. So up he went. But he hadn't been there long before he stuck his head out of his door and shouted downstairs.

'Hey!' he called. 'When a big man like me wants to sit down, where's he to sit?'

'You sit on a chair, Brer Rabbit!' cried the others, 'and don't make such a fuss about it.'

'All right,' said Brer Rabbit. 'But just you look out down there!'

Now Brer Rabbit had taken into his room, without any one knowing, a gun, a cannon, and a mighty big tub, which he had filled with water. He went to the gun and, BANGITY-BANG! He fired it off. All the animals in the parlour jumped up in a fright, and looked at one another, trembling.

'Brer Rabbit sits down mighty hard,' said Brer Bear. Then the door above opened, and Brer Rabbit stuck his head out again.

'When a big man like me wants to sneeze, where shall he sneeze?' he called.

'Where you like!' roared the animals.

'Look out down there, then!' said Brer Rabbit, and with that he let off his cannon, BOOM-BOOM! The animals nearly jumped out of their skins, and Brer Bear fled out of the door.

'Brer Rabbit's got a mighty bad cold,' said Brer Wolf. Then the door above opened again, and Brer Rabbit looked out.

'When a big man like me wants to rinse out his tea-cup, where shall he throw the water?' he called.

'Where you please!' shouted back the animals.

'Look out down there, then!' cried Brer Rabbit, and he tilted over the big tub of water. Down the stairs it poured in a rush, and flowed into the parlour. All the animals jumped up, shouting with fright, and rushed out of the house in a terrible hurry. Brer Fox leapt out of the window, and Brer Wolf ran through the back door. The rest went out of the front door, and soon Brer Rabbit was left alone.

He locked up the doors and shut the windows. Then, with a broad grin on his face, the rogue cuddled down into his bed and went to sleep with the whole house to himself!

Dame Twiddle's Gold

THERE was once an old woman called Dame Twiddle, whose kitchen chimney needed sweeping. So she poked her brush up – and what should come tumbling down among the soot but ten pieces of gold! How surprised and delighted Dame Twiddle was!

'I must go and tell all my neighbours!' she said. So she popped the gold on the table, put on her shawl, and ran out to tell her friends.

She went to the well where the village women were drawing water and talking.

'Listen to me!' she cried. 'I have found riches up my chimney! What do you think of that?'

'Well, well,' said every one, 'that is good fortune for you. You must keep it safely, though, for there are robbers about. Where have you put it?'

'Oh, I left it on the kitchen table,' said Dame Twiddle.

'How very silly of you!' said her friends. 'Come with us and we will show you a strong bag in the village shop. You can buy it to put your money in.'

So Dame Twiddle went to the shop and saw the bag.

'I will have it,' she said. 'It will keep my money safe.'

'But if thieves come they can easily carry the bag away,' said the shopkeeper. 'See, put your money in the bag, and then buy a good strong box to put the bag in. A robber will not be likely to carry away a heavy box. What do you think of this one? It is the strongest I have.'

'It is a fine box,' said the old dame. 'I will have it. I am sure no robber would carry that away. Why, I can hardly lift one end of it. My riches will be safe there.'

'Have you a key to lock your cottage when you go out?' asked her friends. 'If you don't lock your door robbers may come while you are out marketing, and two men could lift that box, you know. You had better buy a new lock and key for your door. Then you and your money will be quite safe.'

'I have a strong new lock and key here,' said the shopkeeper, and he showed her a brand-new one, bright and shining. 'No robber will be able to enter when you have this on your door.'

'I will have that lock and key,' said the old dame. 'Then I shall feel that my riches are safe.'

'I will bring everything along to your cottage now,' said the shopkeeper. So he and his boy carried the box. Dame Twiddle carried the strong bag, and in it she put the lock and key. When they got home the shopkeeper put the lock on the door. Then he asked to be paid.

'I want two pounds for the bag,' he said, 'and six pounds for the big box, and one pound for the lock and key, and one pound for my trouble.'

Dame Twiddle paid him, and he went. Then she thought she would put her riches into the bag, and the bag into the box, where it would be safe. But hunt as she might she couldn't find a single piece of gold anywhere! Do *you* know what she had done with it?

The Sillies

IN the very heart of Wishing Wood stands a fine hazel tree. Every year it bears hundreds of nuts, each neatly wrapped up in a green cloak. This year it has more nuts than ever.

Early one morning two squirrels discovered it.

'This shall be *our* nut-tree,' they said. 'We will take the nuts and bury them in the ground near by. Then when we wake in the winter-time we shall have a fine feast.'

But just at that moment three little dormice ran up the tree and scampered along the branch on which the squirrels sat.

'This is *our* nut-tree,' they said. 'It belonged to our father and grandfather and great-grandfather. Every year we dormice come and feast on the nuts to make ourselves nice and fat before we go to sleep for the long, cold winter.

'*Your* nut-tree!' said the squirrels scornfully. 'What do you mean, *your* nut-tree! It's ours, and we mean to pick every nut there is and store them for ourselves. So just run away, you little snippets!'

The three dormice were very angry. They ran at the squirrels, but, of course, they were too tiny to push them off the tree. Just as they were wondering what to do next there came a great flip-flap of wings, and down came the nuthatch bird, smartly dressed in grey and chestnut.

'Tooee, tooee, tooee!' he whistled. 'What is all this to-do in my tree?'

'*Your* tree!' cried the squirrels and the dormice, in a rage. 'What next! This is *our* tree!'

'Nonsense!' said the nuthatch, pecking at a fat cluster of nuts. 'I always come to this tree in the autumn, for I fancy a few hazel-nuts then.'

Well, the squirrels and the dormice were not going to have that! Dear me, no! They raised their voices and called one another horrid names till the wood echoed with their cries.

Two children, who were out nutting, heard them, and ran to see what was the matter. As soon as the animals and bird saw the children they became silent, and peered down at them in fright.

'Oh, the sillies!' said the little girl. 'They are all quarrelling about who shall have the nuts! And there are more than enough for all of them.'

'Well, *we'll* have them now!' said the boy. He picked as many as he could reach, and soon the two baskets were full to the brim.

'Shall we fill our pockets too?' said the little girl.

'No,' said the boy. 'We'll leave the rest of the nuts for the little squabblers! They are looking rather sad.'

They went away, and then out crept the squirrels, the dormice, and the nuthatch.

'We'll share them,' said a dormouse in a humble voice. 'Haven't we been great big sillies?'

And I really think they had, don't you?

The Runaway Goats

A Very Old Story

THERE was once a little girl who minded goats. She had to take them to the hills each morning, watch them all day, and bring them home again in the evening. On the way to the hills she always passed a field of corn, and was careful to see that the goats did not run into it.

But one evening they ran away, and went to the field of corn. The little girl was cross with them, and afraid that the farmer would come and scold her.

'Goats, goats, come out of the field!' she cried. 'How *dare* you spoil the corn!'

But the goats took no notice at all. They just went on eating their fill. Then the little girl began to cry bitterly. Soon a rabbit came up and asked her why she cried, and she told him.

'*I'll* get them out of the field for you!' said the rabbit. So he ran to the goats, crying, 'Goats, goats, come out of the field! How *dare* you spoil the corn!'

But the goats took no notice at all. They just went on eating their fill. Then the rabbit began to cry bitterly, and he and the little girl sobbed together. Soon a fox came up and asked them why they cried. The rabbit told him.

'*I'll* get them out of the field for you!' said the fox. So he ran to the goats, crying, 'Goats, goats, come out of the field! How *dare* you spoil the corn!'

But the goats took no notice at all. They just went on eating their fill. Then the fox began to cry bitterly, and he and the rabbit and the little girl sobbed together. Soon a dog came up and asked them why they cried. The fox told him.

'*I'll* get them out of the field for you!' said the dog. So he ran to the goats, crying, 'Goats, goats, come out of the field! How *dare* you spoil the corn!'

But the goats took no notice at all. They just went on eating their fill. Then the dog began to cry bitterly, and he and the fox and the rabbit and the little girl sobbed together.

Soon a wasp flew up with a buzz-zz-zz and asked them why they cried. The dog told him.

'*I'll* get them out of the field for you!' said the wasp. So he flew into the field and buzzed up to the goats. 'Goats, goats, come out of the field!

How *dare* you spoil the corn!'

But the goats took no notice at all. They just went on eating their fill. Then the wasp said 'BUZZ!' and stung the first goat on his ear. He said 'BUZZ!' and stung the second goat on his tail. He said 'BUZZ!' and stung the third one on his back. He said 'BUZZ!' and stung the last one on his nose.

And with one accord all the goats began to bleat loudly, and rushed out of the cornfield.

'Little creatures can sometimes do big things!' said the wasp, and off he went with a very loud BUZZ.

The Greedy Yellowhammer

SILVERTOES was most excited. She was giving a party to the birds, the rabbits and the elves of Hawthorn Wood, and she was buying all the cakes.

'Let me see,' she said. 'I'll have twelve chocolate buns, twenty lettuces for the rabbits, and six of those big seed-cakes for the birds. Here, Whiskers, put them in your basket, there's a dear!'

Whiskers was her servant, a little brown mouse, very hard-working and faithful. Silvertoes made up her mind to buy a nice yellow cheese for him to eat at the party, so she went to the grocer's. There she bought a perfectly lovely cheese, and when she got home she hid it on the window-sill outside the parlour, for she wanted it to be a surprise for Whiskers the next day. She didn't like to hide it anywhere *inside* her cottage, for Whiskers dusted so well that he would be sure to find it.

Now early the next morning Goldie the

yellowhammer came flying by. He saw the cheese on the window-sill and flew down to have a look. He had never tasted cheese in his life, so he took a peck at it. It *was* good! Goldie took another peck, and swallowed a bigger piece.

He guessed it was something for the party, but he was a greedy little bird and somehow he couldn't stop pecking at that cheese. He made great holes in it, and very soon the cheese began to look much smaller, and very untidy.

Suddenly Goldie heard a noise, and off he flew in a hurry. He perched in a hawthorn bush and thought about the cheese – and suddenly he began to feel rather queer. He had eaten far too much, and, oh dear me, he *did* feel ill! All day long he sat and groaned, feeling quite certain he would never be able to go to Silvertoes' party.

The party began at four o'clock, and all the guests arrived punctually, except Goldie. Whiskers made the tea, and soon every one was busy munching and pecking. Suddenly Silvertoes remembered the cheese she had hidden.

But how upset she was to find it nearly all gone! Whoever could have been so greedy? She carried the bit that was left into her parlour, and told all her guests what had happened. They were very much shocked, for it was dreadful to think that there was a thief in Hawthorn Wood.

Just as the clock struck five, and everything was eaten except some bread and the piece of cheese, Goldie the yellowhammer flew in at the door. He was feeling a bit better, so he thought he would go to the party after all.

'Oh, dear!' cried Silvertoes, in dismay. 'We've eaten everything, Goldie, dear. I'm afraid we can only offer you bread and cheese. Would you like that?'

At the sound of cheese Goldie turned pale. He knew that he could never touch cheese again, for he had been so ill.

'A little bit of bread and *NO* cheese!' he said. Then everybody guessed that it was he who had stolen the cheese, and they turned away from him in scorn. Goldie flew away in shame, and hid his head for many a day. And when he joined the others again, what do you think he sang – why, nothing but this: 'Little bit of bread and *NO* cheese! Little bit of bread and *NO* cheese!'

He still sings it – you can hear him any day in the hedgerows!

Snippysnap the Tailor

ONE very warm February morning Mr Snippy-snap the Pixie tailor went along the lane that ran by the farm belonging to the Goblin King. He was very hot, so when he saw a gap in the hedge, he crawled through it and sat himself down under the shady branches of an elm-tree.

In the field were fifty-three young lambs. Their coats were thick and their tails were long. The sun warmed them, and made them feel very hot indeed. When they saw Snippysnap they came over to speak to him.

'Isn't it hot?' they said. 'Shall we ever get cool?'

'Oh, yes,' said Snippysnap. 'When the summer comes the shepherd will bring out his shears and snip your heavy coats off. Then you will be nice and cool.'

'O-o-h!' said the lambs. 'Please, Snippysnap, would you cut off our coats for us *now*? And our tails, too? We are much too hot. You would be doing a good deed to us, really you would.'

Well, Snippysnap was a foolish little tailor, and he didn't stop to think that the weather would almost certainly turn cold again, and then the lambs would shiver and freeze. He smiled, and said he would do just what they wanted him to.

'I'll do your tails first,' he said. 'Stand with your backs to me, in a row, and I shan't take long.'

They did as they were told, and soon Snippysnap had a big armful of soft tails. Just as he was going to start on their coats, he saw the shepherd coming. Then Snippysnap was afraid, and he ran away as fast as he could, carrying the tails with him.

The shepherd saw what had happened, and chased Snippysnap, waving his crook in anger. The little tailor threw his armful of tails into the hedge, and ran on for all he was worth. But he couldn't escape the shepherd!

He was caught and spanked hard with the shepherd's crook.

'Where are all those tails you cut off?' demanded the shepherd.

'I th-th-threw them into the hedge,' wept Snippysnap.

'Go and get them,' said the shepherd; but,

dear me, when the little tailor went to fetch them, what do you think had happened? Why, they had all grown on to the big hazel-bushes in the hedge, and were wriggling and dancing in the wind for all the world as if they were still on the lambs!

'O-o-h!' said Snippysnap. 'Just look at that! The lambs' tails have grown on to the hazel-tree! Won't the children be pleased!'

And to this day you'll find lambs' tails growing on the hazel in February! Don't forget to look, will you?

Brer Rabbit and Mr Dog

ONE day the animals all had a meeting, and every one was there. There was Brer Fox next to Brer Wolf, Brer Bear, Brer Hare, Brer Possum, Brer Turkey-Buzzard, Brer Terrapin, and a whole heap more. Brer Rabbit was there, too, and he sat next to Mr Dog.

Now Mr Dog had very big teeth indeed, and every time he opened his mouth to speak, Brer Rabbit got a glimpse of them, and he felt mighty scared. He jumped in fright when he saw them, and when Mr Dog turned to see what was the matter with Brer Rabbit, Brer Rabbit jumped all the more.

Then the animals began to laugh, because Brer Rabbit looked so funny, but Mr Dog thought they were laughing at *him*. He growled and showed all his teeth again, and Brer Rabbit slipped to one side and shivered like a jelly.

'Ho, ho!' laughed the animals, thinking it was a great joke to see Brer Rabbit afraid. Mr Dog growled more loudly when he heard all the laughter, and he snapped at Brer Rabbit, who gave a tremendous yell and scuttled away as fast as he could.

That broke up the meeting, and all the animals went home laughing. At the next meeting Brer Rabbit got up and spoke.

'I think that all those animals who have large teeth ought to have their mouths sewn up,' he said. 'There's Brer Fox, he's got great teeth, and so has Brer Wolf. And Mr Dog's teeth are worse than anybody's. *His* mouth ought to be sewn up first of all.'

Then Mr Lion, who was at the head of the meeting, spoke up.

'Very well,' he said; 'we will have Mr Dog's mouth sewn up, and then he can't frighten any one with his great teeth. But who's going to sew him up?'

Nobody spoke for a minute. Then Brer Bear said, 'Seems to me that the one to sew up Mr Dog's mouth is the one who wants it done – and that's Brer Rabbit.'

'Yes, let Brer Rabbit do it!' everybody cried. *Now* Brer Rabbit was in a fix! He didn't dare to sew up Mr Dog's mouth, and yet he didn't want to show he was afraid.

'I haven't got a needle,' he said. Brer Bear

fetched one. 'And now I haven't got any thread,' said Brer Rabbit. Brer Wolf fetched some. Brer Rabbit took it and very carefully threaded the needle. Then he marched up to Mr Dog, who was sitting back on his haunches, snarling horribly.

'I'll have to get some one to hold Mr Dog while I sew his mouth,' said Brer Rabbit. 'One of you come and hold him.'

But nobody would hold Mr Dog. Then Brer Rabbit threw down the needle and thread and stamped his foot.

'You're a set of cowards!' he said. 'I'm the only brave man among you!'

And with that he walked away, his head in the air, and not one of the animals guessed that he wouldn't have sewn up Mr Dog's mouth for anything in the world! Oh, clever Brer Rabbit!

The Twelfth Fisherman

A Tale of the Men of Gotham

ONCE upon a time twelve men of Gotham went out fishing. Some of them fished from the dry bank, and some of them waded out into the river. When the day ended, they all gathered together to go home.

'Twelve of us started out this morning,' said one. 'Let us hope that there are twelve to go home, for it would be a dreadful thing if one of us were drowned.'

'We will count and see,' said another man. So he began to count, touching each of his friends as he did so. But he quite forgot to count himself, so it seemed to him as if there were only eleven fishermen.

'Let *me* count,' said a third man. So he began to count his friends too, but he also forgot to count himself, and to his dismay there were only eleven. Then each man counted, and as not one remembered to add himself, they could make no more than eleven.

'Alas! Alas!' cried they. 'One of us is drowned! Let us go back to the river.'

So they all went back to the river, but they could see no one in the water at all. They groaned and cried, and wrung their hands in grief, for they were full of distress to think that one of their number was drowned.

Now a courtier came riding by just then, and he heard all the groaning and crying. He was very much astonished, and he rode up to ask what was the matter.

'What are you seeking?' he asked. 'And why do you weep so bitterly?'

'Sir,' answered the men of Gotham, 'twelve of us started out this morning to fish, and we fear that one of us is drowned.'

'Now this is strange,' said the courtier. 'Count how many there are of you!'

So one of the men counted his eleven friends, but he did not count himself, and this made the courtier smile.

'What will you give me if I find your twelfth man for you?' he asked.

The men of Gotham took all the money they had and put it into a bag. 'See,' they said, 'you shall have all this if you find our twelfth man.'

'Give me the bag,' said the courtier, so they

gave it to him, and he tied it to his saddle.

'Now,' said he, 'come round me and I will find you your twelfth man.' They came round and he began to count, whacking each man over the shoulders as he did so. 'One – two – three – four – five – six – seven – eight – nine – ten – eleven – *twelve*. Here is your twelfth man! I have found him for you!'

'Now may good fortune follow you all the days of your life!' cried the men of Gotham in joy. 'You have found our friend for us! Our blessings go with you!'

Then, with a laugh, the courtier spurred his horse and went on his way, the bag of money jingling merrily as he rode – but the men of Gotham did not know why he laughed!

The Man, His Boy, and the Donkey

A Tale From Aesop's Fables

'WE will take our donkey to market today and sell it,' said a man to his son. 'Go and fetch it, boy, and we will start now.'

The boy brought the donkey to his father and the two set off to walk to market. Soon they met a youth who laughed when he saw them.

'Why do you walk?' he cried. 'Why do you not ride the donkey, O, stupid ones?'

'Get up on the donkey's back,' said the man to his boy. 'I will not have people laughing at us.'

So up the boy got, and once more they went on their way. Soon they met a lusty farmer, riding on his horse.

'For shame!' he cried, when he saw the three coming along. 'You are young and strong, my boy, and yet you ride whilst your poor old father walks!'

'Get down and *I* will ride,' said the man to his son. 'I will not have people crying shame on you!'

So the boy got down and the man mounted the donkey.

Soon they met an old woman, and she pointed her finger in anger at the man.

'See!' she cried to her daughter. 'Look at that great strong man riding, whilst his poor little boy walks in the dust! What a cruel father he must be!'

The man was in despair. No matter what he did it seemed to be wrong.

'Get up beside me,' he said to his son. 'We will ride together on the donkey, and then no one can say anything.'

So the boy got up behind his father, and together they jogged on their way. Soon they met a girl.

'How can you treat your poor donkey so?' she cried. 'Two people on one poor animal! See how he hangs his head, poor beast! You should carry him, not he you!'

The two got down and fetched a strong pole. They turned the donkey upside down and strapped his four feet to it. Then they each took an end upon their shoulder. They started off again for the market, carrying the heavy donkey, panting and groaning with his great weight.

As they entered the town the children came crowding around, astonished to see a donkey being carried in this way.

'Ho! Look at him!' cried one. 'What a funny sight!'

Then all the children began to laugh and shout so loudly that the donkey was terrified. He kicked his feet free, turned the right way up, and galloped off as fast as he could go.

'There!' said the man in anger. 'We have lost our donkey! Why did we try to please everybody? We have ended in pleasing nobody – not even ourselves! I shall do what *I* think next time, no matter what any one says!'

The Axe in the Ceiling

An Old English Tale

THERE was once a farmer who lived with his daughter and wife on a farm. The maiden was loved by a fine gentleman, who came to supper with them every evening, and each night she was sent down to the cellar to get the cider in a jug. She popped down the cellar steps, turned the tap of the cider barrel, filled her jug, and ran upstairs again in a twinkling.

Now one night the daughter went to draw the cider, and as she stood waiting for the jug to fill she happened to glance up at the ceiling – and there, stuck in a wooden beam, she saw an axe. She looked at it, and then she sat down on a stool, threw her apron over her head, and began to weep and wail.

'Oh, my, oh, my!' she cried. 'Suppose I married my fine gentleman, and we had a son, and the son grew up and came down here to draw cider and the axe fell on his head and killed him, oh, what a dreadful thing that would be!'

Now the three upstairs were waiting for the cider, and they wondered what had happened to the maiden. So the mother ran down into the cellar to find out.

'Why, what's the matter?' she asked her daughter in astonishment.

'Oh, mother!' said the girl, 'look at that horrid axe up there! Suppose I married my fine gentleman and we had a son, and he grew up and came down here to draw cider, and the axe fell on him and killed him, wouldn't that be a dreadful thing?'

Then the mother began to weep and wail too, and the farmer upstairs heard the noise and came down to see what was the matter.

'Oh, John!' said his wife, 'do you see that horrid axe up there? Well, suppose our girl married her fine gentleman and they had a son, and he grew up and came down here to draw cider, and the axe fell on him and killed him, wouldn't that be a dreadful thing?'

Then the farmer began to sob and cry too. All this while the fine gentleman had been waiting for his cider, and at last he too went down into the cellar to find out what had happened to every one.

'Oh, friend!' said the farmer, 'do look at that

horrid axe up there! Suppose you married my daughter and had a son, and he grew up and came down here to draw cider, and the axe fell on his head and killed him, wouldn't that be a dreadful thing?'

'Well,' said the gentleman with a laugh, 'is that all that is worrying you? I can soon put matters right!'

And with that he reached up and took the axe from the wooden beam and threw it on the ground. Then he turned off the cider tap, for the jug was filled and the cider was running all over the floor.

'Never in my life have I seen three such sillies!' said the fine gentleman. 'I am now going to set out on my travels, and if I find three greater sillies than you, well, I will come back and marry your daughter!'

What the Traveller Found

The Axe in the Ceiling continued

THE fine gentleman set out on his travels to see if he could find three greater sillies than the ones he had left behind. At last he came to a cottage built against a hillside, and to his great surprise he saw an old woman there trying to make her cow go up a ladder to the roof of her cottage.

'You see, there is grass growing there,' she said. 'I thought if I got the cow on the roof she could eat it. I shall tie a rope round her neck, and the other end I shall put down the chimney and tie to my wrist. Then if the cow falls I shall know.'

'But wouldn't it be easier to cut the grass and throw it down to the cow?' asked the traveller. The old woman took no notice of his advice, but got the poor cow on to the roof. She popped the rope down the chimney, climbed off the roof, and went into the cottage. She tied the rope round her wrist – and at that very moment the cow fell off the roof! The old dame was dragged half-way up the chimney and there she stuck in the soot, whilst the miserable cow hung half-way between roof and ground. The traveller cut the rope and went on his way, thinking that he had found *one* big silly.

That night he stayed at an inn, and shared a bed with another man. In the morning he was surprised to see this man hang his trousers on the knob of the chest of drawers, and then run across the room and try to jump into them. This he did for about half an hour, and got very tired.

'Trousers really are the most awkward clothes ever invented!' said the man. 'It takes me all morning to jump into mine!'

'But why don't you draw them on like this?' asked the traveller, and he showed the man what to do. Then off he went on his travels again, thinking that he had found *another* big silly.

That evening he came to a village in the middle of which was a pond. The villagers were raking in the water with brooms, hoes, forks, and rakes, and the traveller asked what they were doing.

'Why, the moon has fallen into our pond,' said the villagers. 'We saw her shining there as plain as could be. We must get her out or she will drown.'

'But the moon is in the sky!' said the traveller, beginning to laugh. 'See, there she is! You are only trying to get out her reflection, and you can't do that!'

But the villagers wouldn't listen to him, and drove him away with their forks and rakes. The traveller mounted his horse again and turned its head homewards.

'Well,' he said, 'I have certainly found three greater sillies than the farmer, his wife, and daughter. So I must go back and marry the maiden.'

And back he went and married the daughter, and, so people say, they lived happily ever after.

Cuckoo! Cuckoo!

ONCE upon a time the Men of Gotham heard the cuckoo calling for the first time that year, and they were glad. 'Ah!' they said, 'spring is here again! We know that spring is here because the cuckoo is calling.'

'What a pity we cannot have springtime all the year round,' said one man. 'I hate the winter with its snow and ice. Is there no way we might always have the lovely springtime with us?'

The Men of Gotham sat and thought for a long time. Then one of them sprang up with a shout. 'I have it!' he cried. 'It is always springtime when the cuckoo comes. Let us catch a cuckoo and make him stay with us all the year round – then we shall have spring days all the time. Is not this a good idea, my brothers?'

The Men of Gotham were pleased. They began to talk of how they might keep the cuckoo captive. One of them remembered a little copse in the middle of the town, a thicket of small trees and bushes. He thought it would be a very nice place for the cuckoo to live. 'We could build a thick fence all round,' he said. 'Then the cuckoo could not get away, and we should hear it cuckooing all through the town, and springtime would always be with us.'

'We will do this!' cried the Men of Gotham, and together they ran to build the fence. When it was finished they went to the woods to find a cuckoo. This was not easy, for although they could hear the cuckoo's pretty double-note all round them, they could not see him. But at last they caught a fine big one, and brought him to the town, cuckooing loudly in fright all the time. They put him in the very middle of the copse, and then shut the gate in the thick fence they had built around.

They were very happy. They joined hands and danced round the fence, singing:

Sing, cuckoo, sing,
Now we shall have spring,
What a happy thing,
Sing, cuckoo, sing.

But the cuckoo sang never a note, for it was much too frightened. It hid in a bush, and was quite silent and dumb. Soon the people went away to bed, and the cuckoo slept. But when dawn came the people came back again, and danced round the fence once more, begging the cuckoo to sing.

Then the bird grew tired of being in the copse, and spread its big wings. 'Cuckoo! Cuckoo!' it cried loudly, and flew right over the fence back to the wood where it had come from.

'Oh, oh!' cried the people in dismay. 'We did not make the fence high enough. Next time we will build it twice as high! Now we have lost the springtime!'

'Cuckoo! Cuckoo!' sang the cuckoo. 'You are cuckoos, cuckoos! Oh, cuckoo, cuckoo!'

But the Men of Gotham didn't listen. They thought they were very wise indeed; but I agree with the cuckoo, don't you?

The Singing Kettle

ONCE upon a time old Dame Kitkat stole a spell from the Wizard Woolla-malee. It was a very powerful spell, made to give any one owning it a beautiful singing voice. Dame Kitkat wanted it to sell to a famous singer who had lost her voice.

'I shall ask a big sack of gold!' thought the greedy old woman gleefully. 'My, how rich I shall be!'

She took the spell home and popped it on her kitchen table. It was a little yellow thing no bigger than a pea. Whoever swallowed it would sing like a nightingale, for it was made of the loveliest sounds in the world – a baby's laugh, the sound of a little waterfall, the hum of a bee, the deepest note of a blackbird, and every other lovely thing you can think of.

But, goodness gracious me, what a shock the old dame got – for who should she see come hobbling down her garden path but the great Wizard Woolla-malee himself! And he knew she had stolen the spell from him, for he had been told so by his next-door neighbour! He shook his stick in the air and growled and grunted as he went up the path. Dame Kitkat shivered in her great big shoes, and caught up the spell in a hurry.

'Where shall I hide it?' she wondered. 'Oh, I'll put it in my kettle on the stove. The wizard will never think of looking there!'

So she did, and when the wizard came in she was very busy dusting her larder.

'Now, now, now!' said Woolla-malee, shaking his stick again. 'Where have you hidden my spell?'

'I don't know what you are talking about!' said Dame Kitkat, looking most surprised. 'If you think I've hidden anything of yours, you're quite welcome to look for it!'

Then Woolla-malee began hunting – and how he searched and poked and peered and peeped! But it wasn't a bit of good, he couldn't find his spell.

'I'm tired,' he said at last. 'Give me a cup of tea, Kitkat.'

The old dame popped her kettle right over the fire to boil the water, smiling to think that the spell was there, and the wizard didn't know it –

but, oh, dear me, what a shock she got! For no sooner did the kettle begin to boil than it started to sing! And this is the song it sang:

Zee, zee, zee, ZEE.
Dear Woolla-malee,
I'm boiling, I'm boiling,
I'm toiling and moiling,
I'm all of a bubble,
A bubble, a hubble,
Oh, zee, zee, zee, ZEE.
Take pity on me,
Dear Woolla-malee!

'Ho!' cried the wizard in a fury, and ran to the kettle – but alas! the spell was all boiled away, and was no longer there. Woolla-malee turned to scold the dame, but she jumped on her broomstick in fright and sailed away to the new moon. You may be sure that no one ever saw *her* again!

But the funny thing is that ever since that day kettles have always sung a little song when they begin to boil. Have you heard it? Listen hard, and you're sure to hear it beginning its little 'Zee, zee, zee, ZEE!'

Goblin Glue

THERE was once a goblin called Waitabit, who invented a very strong glue. All the fairy folk were pleased, because when they broke a dish, or a plate, it could be mended at once.

Now one day there came a very high wind, which blew so strongly that it sent chimney-pots flying off everywhere.

'Oh, my, oh, my!' sighed the Lord High Chamberlain when complaints came in. 'Here's a fine to-do! However am I going to get all the chimney-pots fixed on again?'

'*I* know what we can do!' said his wife. 'What about that goblin glue? It's quite cheap – only a halfpenny for a large pot. It's so very strong that I am sure every one could stick chimney-pots on with it, and make them so firm they never fly off again!'

'Splendid idea!' said the Chamberlain. 'The goblin glue is *just* the thing for chimney-pots!'

So he made a proclamation telling every one to use the goblin glue, and get their houses right again as quickly as possible. Then the people took their halfpennies and went to buy the glue from Waitabit.

But that goblin was very sharp.

'Wait a bit, wait a bit,' he said. 'My glue's gone up in price. It's a *shilling* a pot now!'

Well, everybody grumbled, but since the Chamberlain had ordered them to buy it, they could do nothing else but pay the terrible price that Waitabit asked.

Now the goblin hadn't nearly enough to go round, so he took all the strong glue he had got, and made it much weaker, by pouring water into it. Then he had enough for every one – but you may be sure he didn't say a word about what he had done!

All the little folk trotted off home with their glue, and set to work to stick their chimney-pots on again. But, oh, dear me, in the middle of the night a little wind got up, and blew off all the chimney-pots again quite easily.

In a furious rage the Chamberlain drove to the goblin's cave. Waitabit had just made a tremendous lot of new glue, and was busy making it weak with water. The Chamberlain caught him, and shouted at him so loudly that the goblin nearly fell into a glue-vat.

'So this is what you do, is it!' said the Chamberlain. 'Just because every one wants what you sell, you put the price up to a shilling, and make your glue four times weaker! You are a horrid little goblin, and I shall punish you well. You shall be –'

But Waitabit didn't stop to hear what his punishment was to be. He gave a frightened howl, leaped into the air, turned into smoke and disappeared!

But he left all his glue behind him, and for a long time the Chamberlain didn't know what to do with it. Then his wife had a fine idea.

'What about putting it on all the horse-chestnut buds?' she said. 'You know how they complain of the frost? Well, the glue would protect them nicely!'

And so it does. It is terribly sticky – just take hold of a bud and see!

The King With the Ass's Ears

An Old Greek Tale

HAVE you heard the reeds whispering in the wind, when you walk by a pond or river? They are dry and rustly, and whisper loudly when the wind blows. Do you know what they say? This story will tell you.

Once upon a time there lived a king called Midas. He was in the fields one day, when the god Pan challenged the god Apollo to make better music than he did. Midas was to be the judge.

Pan played first, merry tunes, shrill and lilting, on his pipe. Then Apollo swept his hand across his lyre, and made such glorious music that everything paused to listen. Even the swallows ceased their endless flying, and hovered round to hear.

But Midas, who admired Pan and wanted to please him, chose to give him the prize. Apollo was very angry, for he knew the king had been unjust.

'Cannot you tell beautiful music when you hear it?' he cried. 'What is the matter with your ears, O Midas? Are they not big enough to take in the lovely notes of my lyre? Let me make them larger!'

At once Midas felt something queer happening to his head. His ears grew long and upright, fur appeared upon them, and he found that he could move them about! What had happened to them!

He ran to a nearby pool and looked in the water to see himself. Alas for him! He had ass's ears!

In rage and horror he ran back to his palace. What would his people say when they saw him?

'My barber shall make me a wig!' he thought. 'It will be a high one, and then it will hide these terrible ears.'

So he called his barber to him and bade him make the wig. The barber was horrified when he saw the ass's ears growing on the king's head, and stared at them in amazement.

'Keep my secret,' commanded the king. 'If you do not, you shall be put to death. No one but you must know of this terrible thing.'

The barber promised faithfully to tell no one. He made a beautiful wig that entirely hid the king's ears, and then left the palace.

He found it very difficult to keep the king's secret. He longed to tell it to some one. He dared not say anything, even to his wife, for he knew that such a secret would at once fly all over the kingdom.

Time went on, and the barber felt his secret lie so heavily on him that he could neither eat nor sleep. He must tell some one, or he would go mad. So he went to a far-away field by the river, and dug a deep hole. Then, bending down, he whispered the king's secret into the hole: 'Midas has ass's ears!'

After that he went home happy. But soon reeds grew up and covered the hole, and then, when the wind blew over them, they bent towards each other and whispered, 'Midas has ass's ears! Midas has ass's ears!'

Soon every one in the kingdom knew the king's secret, though Midas never guessed how it was spread abroad. And ever since that day the reeds have whispered the same thing. You can hear them plainly if you listen: 'Midas has ass's ears-s-s-s, Midas has-s-s-s ass's ears-s-s-s.'

The Donkey that Laughed

MR STRAWS, the farmer, had a donkey that pulled him along in a little cart. The donkey was called Gray, and was as sharp as a needle, though Mr Straws always called him a stupid creature.

One market day Mr Straws had done all his business, and was going home in his little donkey-cart. On the way he overtook Mr Twinkle, who was carrying a sack over his shoulder.

'Hey, Mr Twinkle!' called Mr Straws. 'Are you going my way?'

'Yes,' said Mr Twinkle. 'Will you give me a lift? My legs are tired. Shall I be too heavy for your little donkey?'

'Oh, no,' said Mr Straws. 'He's had a hard day, but there's plenty of go in him yet. Climb up, Mr Twinkle.'

So Mr Twinkle climbed up into the little donkey-cart and sat down. He didn't take his sack from his shoulder though – he still held it there, and the potatoes were so heavy that they almost bent him double with their weight.

'Wouldn't you like to put that sack down?' asked Mr Straws.

'Yes, I should,' said Mr Twinkle. 'But that donkey of yours is tired, and it's bad enough for him to have to carry *me* – I won't bother him to carry my potatoes too; I'll carry them myself.'

'That's kind of you,' said Mr Straws.

The donkey suddenly stopped in the road and said, 'Hee-haw, hee-hee-haw!'

'It sounds just as if he's laughing!' said Mr Twinkle. 'I wonder what the joke is.'

The donkey went on, but he went more slowly than before, and Mr Straws began to think he would be late for supper.

'Get up there!' he shouted to the donkey, and he jerked the reins. But the obstinate creature wouldn't go any faster, and Mr Straws became angry.

'Ho!' he said. 'This is how you return Mr Twinkle's kindness, is it? You think you'll make us late for supper. Get on now!'

But still the donkey wouldn't go fast. Then Mr Straws quite lost his temper. He turned to Mr Twinkle.

'Put your sack of potatoes down in the cart!'

he said. 'The donkey can carry that too! I'll show him who's master! He'll be sorry when he feels the extra weight of the sack!'

So Mr Twinkle slid the sack from his shoulder to the floor of the cart, and how glad he was to get rid of the weight!

But was the donkey sad? Not a bit of it! He laughed even more loudly than before. 'Heehaw, hee-hee-haw!' he went. 'Hee-haw, HEE-HAW!'

'Bless us!' said Mr Straws. 'What's the joke *now*? *I* don't know – do you, Mr Twinkle?'

I wonder if *you* know what the donkey was laughing at?

Coo-Roo, the Vain Pigeon

THERE was once a pretty wood-pigeon called Coo-Roo, who thought herself far too clever to live with her brothers and sisters. She thought she would go and live with some clever animal, who would praise her for her sharp wits. So one day she flew off to where Sly-One the fox lived, for she knew he was clever.

'May I live with you?' she asked Sly-One, flying down beside him. 'I am clever and pretty, and I am sure you would enjoy my company.'

'I don't care whether you are clever or pretty, so long as you are *plump*,' said Sly-One looking at Coo-Roo in such an odd way that she was frightened, and hopped a little distance off. Then she saw Sly-One's gleaming white teeth, and she flew off in a panic, for she knew why the fox wanted her to be plump.

'Nasty creature,' she said to herself. 'I'll go and find some one far cleverer than *he* is! Now what about Tibbles, the big white cat? I heard his mistress say the other day that she was sure he was the cleverest animal in the world. Perhaps he would be honoured to have my company.'

So she flew to Tibbles, the cat, who was warming himself in the sunshine, after a very good dinner of fish and milk.

'May I live with you?' asked Coo-Roo, flying down beside him. 'I am clever and pretty, and I am sure you would enjoy my company.'

'I don't mind whether you are ugly or pretty, so long as you are young and *tender*!' said Tibbles, and he stretched out his sharp claws. 'But I don't want you just now – I've had a very good dinner. Come again at tea-time!'

But Coo-Roo was frightened to see such great claws, and she soon guessed why Tibbles wanted her to be young and tender. So she flew off in a hurry and took care not to go near Tibbles at tea-time.

'Horrid cat!' she said. 'I'll go and live with the farmer up on the hill. Surely the humans, who are the cleverest of all creatures, will be pleased to have my company.'

So she flew to the farm-house on the hill and pecked at the window. A little boy opened it, and she hopped inside. She saw all the farmer's family sitting round the table, eating dinner.

'May I live with you?' she asked. 'I am clever and pretty, and I am sure you would enjoy my company.'

Nobody said anything for a moment. The pigeon hopped on to the table.

'You are not very polite,' she said. 'Why do you not ask me to share your dinner? What are you eating?'

'PIGEON PIE!' said the farmer, and he made a grab at the vain bird. 'You wretched pigeons eat my corn, so we eat *you*!'

But the pigeon flew off with a squawk of fright, and went back to her brothers and sisters. And never again in her life did she think she was clever!

The Foolish Donkey

A Tale From Aesop's Fables

THERE was once a donkey who was used by his master for carrying loads. Every morning he strapped a burden on the animal's back, and then drove him to market in order to sell his wares.

The donkey was young and strong, but he was very lazy. He hated carrying loads, for they made his back ache. He tried to shake them off, but his master only tied them on all the more tightly. Then he tried to roll on the ground and loosen them. The man cut a big stick from the hedge and beat him well.

One day his master bought a great deal of salt very cheaply and resolved to sell it for a good price at the market. So one morning he loaded the donkey with big sacks in which was good white salt. The sacks were heavy, and the donkey brayed sadly. He set off in front of his master, walking more slowly than usual, for he had never had such a heavy load before.

'Get on, now, get on!' cried his master, 'your back is strong and your legs are firm. Was there ever such a stubborn creature as you!'

At that moment the donkey was walking by the side of a river. Suddenly his legs slipped from beneath him and he fell straight into the water. He brayed with fright and struggled to get out. His master pulled at his bridle, and soon the shivering beast was standing safely on the bank again.

But wonder of wonders! His load was so light that he could hardly feel it! What had happened?

'The salt has all melted in the water!' cried the master angrily. 'My load is wasted.'

Now the donkey remembered this, and the next time he went out with a heavy load of salt he again slipped into the water; but this time he did so on purpose, and he brayed with joy to find that once again his load was lighter.

When he had fallen into the river four times running and wasted four loads of good salt, his master became puzzled.

'Oho,' he said, at last. 'So the donkey has discovered that his load is lighter when he falls into the water! He is a lazy scamp, and must be cured.'

The next morning the master strapped a good load on the donkey's back and set off. As soon as the animal reached the river he again slipped and fell into the water. But alas for him! When he at last struggled out he found that his load, instead of being much lighter, was ten times heavier than before!

'You are carrying sponges today, my friend, and not salt!' said the man, with a laugh. 'Now have you learnt your lesson, or must I beat you as well?'

But the donkey had learnt his lesson at last. Never did he fall into the river again, but worked hard and well, and lived happily with his master for the rest of his days.

Brer Rabbit and the Tar-Baby

ONE day Brer Fox took some tar, mixed it with turpentine, and made a thing with a body, arms, legs, and head, that he called a Tar-Baby. He stuck an old hat on the top of it, set it down in the middle of the road, and then went to hide in some bushes to wait till Brer Rabbit came by.

Soon Brer Rabbit came, lippity-clippity, down the road, as saucy as a jay-bird. Brer Fox lay low. Brer Rabbit spied the Tar-Baby, and looked at it in surprise.

'Morning!' said Brer Rabbit. 'Nice day we're having!'

The Tar-Baby said nothing, and Brer Fox lay low.

'How do you feel this morning?' said Brer Rabbit politely. The Tar-Baby said nothing at all. 'Come, come,' said Brer Rabbit. 'Are you deaf? Because if you are, I can shout in your ear.'

The Tar-Baby sat still, and Brer Fox lay low.

'You're stuck-up, that's what you are!' said

Brer Rabbit. 'And I'm going to cure you, see? I'm going to teach you how to speak to folks when they speak to you. If you don't take off your hat and say "How do you do?" I shall slap you hard.'

The Tar-Baby said never a word, and Brer Fox still lay low, though he nearly burst himself with trying not to laugh.

Then blip! Brer Rabbit hit the Tar-Baby on the side of its head. But that's just where he made his mistake – for his fist stuck, and he couldn't draw it back. The tar held it fast.

'If you don't let me loose, I'll hit you again!' said Brer Rabbit, and with that he let fly with his other fist. That stuck fast too. Still the Tar-Baby said nothing, and Brer Fox lay low.

'Turn me loose before I kick you to bits!' shouted Brer Rabbit. But the Tar-Baby said nothing, and just held on tight. So Brer Rabbit kicked out with both his feet, and *they* stuck too!

'You think you're mighty clever, don't you!' said Brer Rabbit. 'Let go, or I'll butt you with my head, and that'll make you squeal!'

Then he butted, and his head got stuck too.

Then out from the bushes came Brer Fox, and he walked up to Brer Rabbit and looked at him.

'Hey-ho, Brer Rabbit!' he said. 'You look rather stuck-up this morning!' Then he rolled on the ground and laughed till he could laugh no more.

'I'll have you for dinner this time, Brer Rabbit!' he said. 'Yes, I'll have you for dinner this time!'

And did he? Ah, that's a story for another time!

Pixie Gloves

ONCE upon a time there came a very hot summer in Pixieland. The sun blazed down week after week, and the pixies puffed and panted all day long. As for the sunshade-makers, they had their busiest time for years, and couldn't make enough sunshades though they worked through the night as well as the day.

The little pixie princess, Peronel, had a dear little sunshade of her own. It kept the sun from burning her face – but it didn't protect her hands.

Now a pixie princess must always have white hands and a fair face, and the Queen was worried when she saw how freckled Peronel's hands were getting. That wouldn't do for a pixie princess at all! Peronel must keep her hands in her pockets, then the sun wouldn't touch them.

But that was something Peronel could *not* do. She must always be playing with this and that, and she simply couldn't remember to keep her hands in her pockets.

'Very well, then, you must wear gloves,' said her mother, and she stepped into her carriage and drove to market to buy a pair of gloves for Peronel.

But, do you know, there wasn't such a thing to be found! Nobody in the whole of the land wore gloves, and very few pixies had even heard of them. So the Queen had to explain what they were.

'They are coverings for each finger and thumb and for the back and front of the hand,' said she. 'Somebody must make me a pair for Peronel.'

The court tailor set to work. He cut out little bits of soft, silky cloth and tried to make the fingers first. He fitted them neatly on Peronel's tiny fingers and thumb, and then thought that he would sew them all together into a glove. But he couldn't make the fingers to fit. To tell the truth, Peronel didn't want to wear gloves, so when the tailor tried to fit her fingers she curled them up and wriggled them about, and made his work very difficult indeed. He made scores and scores, but the naughty little Princess complained that not one of them fitted her tiny fingers.

For three weeks the tailor worked without being able to make the gloves properly.

Hundreds of silky fingers lay about the floor, but no gloves. Then one day the sun disappeared behind a cloud and the rain came. The hot weather was over!

'I don't need gloves now, I don't need gloves!' sang Peronel, dancing in at the tailor's door. 'Mother says I don't need gloves!'

'Then all these little silky fingers are wasted!' said the tailor, with a frown. 'You are a naughty girl, Peronel!'

'I'll show you what to do with them,' cried the princess, kissing him to make him smile. 'Look, we'll hang them down this stalk, and make them grow into flowers!'

She quickly hung them down a tall, green stalk near by – and lo and behold, the little finger-gloves grew! Have you seen them? We call them foxgloves, but really their name is Folk's Gloves, because the Little Folk, the pixies, first made them. Slip one on your little finger and wish a little wish. It may come true!

The Three Wishes

A Tale From France

HERE is a story told to French children which I am sure *you* will like, too.

There once lived a peasant and his wife in an old tumble-down cottage. The man was lazy, and the woman was quarrelsome and greedy. They had very little money, and were always grumbling because they were poor instead of rich.

'If we were rich, we should be happy,' said the man. 'I should not need to work any more.'

'And I could wear fine clothes and eat as much as I wanted!' said the woman. 'We should be contented, indeed!'

'Oh, no, you wouldn't,' said a laughing voice. The woman turned in surprise, and saw a tiny fairy perched on the mantel-piece. 'You, my man, would still be lazy, and lazy people are seldom happy. And you, woman, would still be quarrelsome and greedy, and such people are always miserable, no matter how rich they may be.'

'Nonsense,' said the man. 'Make us rich, little creature, we beg you! Give us three wishes, and we shall be happy!'

The fairy laughed again.

'Very well,' she said, 'you shall have your three wishes. But mark my words – they will be of no use to you, for you will be sure to waste them! Think well before you use them!'

She disappeared, and the couple looked at one another in excitement. 'What shall we wish for?' said the woman. 'Let us think hard, husband. Draw your chair up to the fire, and we will think of some wonderful things to wish for.'

They sat looking into the blazing fire, and the woman warmed her hands by it.

'What a lovely fire!' she said. 'It would cook a fine pudding, husband. What a pity we haven't one! I do wish we had, don't you?'

She had spoken before she had stopped to think. In an instant a treacle pudding tumbled down the chimney!

'You foolish woman!' cried the man in a rage. 'There's a whole wish wasted! I wish the pudding was at the end of your nose, that I do!'

In a twinkling the pudding flew to the end of the woman's nose, and stuck there. It was the man who had spoken without thinking that

time! In vain the poor woman tried
pudding off her nose. She could not move it.

'I didn't mean to say that,' said the man.
'Now we have only one wish left. Let us ask for
riches beyond belief, wife.'

'What use are riches to me, if I have to go
through life with a pudding at the end of my
nose?' said the unhappy woman. 'No, no, husband. I shall wish this pudding away! *That* shall
be the third wish!'

Before her husband could say anything, the
woman shouted loudly, 'I wish this pudding
were gone!'

At once the pudding flew away up the chimney. The two looked at one another, and just as
they were going to quarrel, they heard the
fairy's laughter again.

'Oh, you *are* a foolish pair!' she said. And I
really think they were.

...ckoo Left Behind

Th... ...s once a cuckoo who wouldn't fly away w... ...n autumn came. His friends the swallows and martins were gone long since, and the cuckoos had gone too. They had flown away to warmer lands, where there were plenty of insects for the winter.

'I shall stay here,' said the cuckoo, 'the robin will help me, and so will the thrush, for they tell me that they both stay for the winter. I don't see why I should tire myself out by flying so many thousands of miles away. It is a most ridiculous idea, and very old-fashioned!'

So he stayed. The autumn days were warm and bright, and the sun shone hotly down – but at night it was cold. The cuckoo found a warm spot in an ivy-covered wall, and there he roosted each night.

'How clever I am!' he said. 'There are plenty of insects about in the sunshine, and the ivy is humming day and night with them!'

The ivy was blooming then, and hosts of

insects came for the nectar. The cuckoo had a fine time, for he caught many for his dinner and grew as fat as could be.

But then the frosts came. The ivy blossoms withered, and green berries came in their place. It was cold, cold, cold. The flies disappeared. No moths came. The bees were in their hives. The wasps were dead, all but the queens, and they were fast asleep in a hole underground.

The cuckoo could find nothing to eat. He went to the robin and asked for a worm, but the robin drove him away at once. He went to the thrush and begged for a snail, but the thrush laughed at him, and said he must look after himself.

Then the cuckoo was in a very bad way. He grew thin and weak, and goodness knows what would have happened to him if he hadn't come one day to a tiny cottage where a clockmaker lived. The cuckoo crept inside for warmth and watched the clockmaker at work.

'Let me live with you, and I will cuckoo for you and tell you the time when you wish to know it,' said the cuckoo.

The clockmaker put on his spectacles and looked at the silly cuckoo. Then he made a wooden clock, and built a little room at the top of it.

'See,' he said to the cuckoo. 'Creep in here. You may live there – but whenever the little hand points to an hour, you must fly out and say cuckoo! At one o'clock you must cuckoo once, and at two o'clock twice, and so on. Do you understand?'

'Yes, thank you very much,' said the cuckoo. He flew inside the clock room, and the door shut after him. There he stayed until the next hour, which was four o'clock, and then out he flew and said 'Cuckoo! cuckoo! cuckoo! cuckoo!' four times, just like that.

'Splendid!' said the clockmaker. 'I have made the first cuckoo clock in the world! What a lot of money I shall get!'

And now you know how the first cuckoo clock came to be made!

The Wind and the Sun

A *Tale From* Aesop's Fables

ONCE upon a time the Wind and the Sun had a quarrel.

'I am far stronger than you,' boasted the Wind. 'I can tear down chimneys, pull up trees and send ships scudding before me. You can do none of these things.'

'Yet I am stronger than you,' said the Sun. 'You are foolish, Wind, to quarrel like this.'

'Very well,' said the Wind, blowing a cloud to shreds as he spoke. 'We will have a trial of strength to prove which of us is the stronger. What shall we do?'

'Do you see that traveller down there?' said the Sun. 'He wears a red cloak round his shoulders. Shall we say that whichever of us can get his cloak off first is the stronger of the two?'

'Agreed!' cried the Wind. 'I will try first, and I tell you I shall certainly win!'

The Wind began. First of all he blew very hard round the traveller. He took hold of the man's cloak and pulled at it. He jerked it this way and that. The traveller was afraid it would be blown off, so he tied it more tightly and held it close round his neck, for he was cold.

The Wind blew more strongly still. He called upon the rain, and drenched the man through from top to toe. The traveller shook the drops from himself, pulled his cloak more tightly round him, and went on his way, complaining bitterly.

The Wind grew angry. He blew up a hurricane and spun the man forward, trying to rip his cloak from him. He howled in his ear. He roared for hail to come, and soon the poor man was trying to protect his head from the stinging balls of ice. He was so cold that he wished he had ten cloaks. He took off the belt from his coat and buckled it tightly round his cloak so that it could not possibly be blown away.

The Wind was defeated, and called mockingly upon the Sun to try *his* power.

The Sun shone out and the clouds and mist fled away. The wind was quiet, the rain stopped. The Sun shone very steadily, and his rays began to dry the traveller's wet cloak.

The man unbuckled his belt and let his cloak hang free from his shoulders, so that it might dry easily. Still the Sun shone down with a steady heat. Soon the traveller felt warm, and unbuttoned his cloak at the neck.

The Sun went on shining. The man began to puff and blow, for he grew hot. He fanned himself with his handkerchief, and took off his hat. The Sun shone and shone.

And suddenly, to the Wind's dismay, and the Sun's delight, the traveller threw off his heavy cloak, and went striding on his way without it. He could not bear the heat of it any longer!

'Gently does it!' cried the Sun to the Wind. 'I've won! Roaring and blustering are never much good, you know! Gently does it!'

Brer Rabbit is Tricked

ONE day Brer Rabbit was going down the road shaking his big bushy tail behind him, whistling like a blackbird. In those days his tail was a mighty fine one, as long as a cat's and as bushy as a squirrel's. He was very proud of it.

Soon he met old Brer Fox ambling along with a big string of fish.

'Hey-ho, Brer Rabbit,' said Brer Fox. 'How are you feeling today?'

'Same as yesterday,' said Brer Rabbit. 'Where did you get that nice string of fish, Brer Fox?'

'I caught them,' said Brer Fox.

'Whereabouts?' asked Brer Rabbit.

'Down in the creek,' said Brer Fox.

'How did you catch them?' said Brer Rabbit, who was mighty fond of minnows.

Brer Fox sat down on a log and grinned at Brer Rabbit.

'All you've got to do if you want to catch a string of minnows is to go to the creek after sundown,' said Brer Fox, 'and drop your tail into the water and hold it there till daylight. Then you'll find a whole lot of minnows hanging on to it when you draw it up again.'

Well, Brer Rabbit thought that was fine and easy. He set off to the creek at sunset, and found a good place to let his tail down into. He sat on the bank with his back to the water, and let his tail hang down into a deep pool.

Now the weather was mighty cold, and the water froze hard that night. Brer Rabbit sat there and sat there, feeling all shivery, but he was so keen on getting a tailful of fish that he didn't move once.

By and by day came, and the sun rose. He thought he would pull up his tail and see how many fish he had caught. So he gave a pull – but his tail was fast in the ice. Then he gave another pull – and lo and behold, where was his tail!

Brer Rabbit felt sort of funny behind, and he found that his long tail was gone! He looked into the frozen pond, and there it was, jerked right off and left in the ice!

Then he knew that Brer Fox had tricked him, and he stamped his paws in rage. Off he set back home as fast as ever he could – but on the way he met Brer Fox, who was grinning like anything.

'Didn't you catch any fish?' he shouted. But

Brer Rabbit wouldn't say a word. He just shook his fist and disappeared into his house.

And ever since that day rabbits have had bobtails!

The Story of Echo and Narcissus

An Old Greek Tale

THERE was once a lovely nymph called Echo, who was so fond of chattering that the goddess Juno became very tired of hearing her voice.

'Go and hide yourself away, Echo!' she commanded her. 'And do not come out until someone calls you. You must never speak except to repeat the last words of others!'

Sadly Echo obeyed, and went to the mountains alone. She longed to show herself when hunters came by, but dared not.

One day a beautiful youth came striding up the mountain-side. His name was Narcissus, and he was very good looking. Echo saw him, and at once fell in love with him. How she longed to show herself and tell him all she felt! She followed him on his way – and soon he knew that someone was near, and wondered who it was.

'Who is there?' he cried, stopping suddenly.

'There!' said Echo.

'Do not follow me!' commanded the youth.

'Me!' cried Echo, always repeating his last word. Narcissus was puzzled.

'Come and show yourself to me here!' he commanded.

'Here!' cried Echo gladly, and stepped forth. But, alas! to her great dismay Narcissus did not love her, and bade her go away again. In sadness she prayed to the goddess Venus to punish Narcissus by making him, in his turn, fall in love with someone who did not want him.

Soon Narcissus was thirsty, and when he came to a clear pool, he knelt down to drink – and in the water he saw his own beautiful face! He thought it was the face of a water-nymph looking up at him, and he stretched out his arms to her. The reflection stretched out its arms too, and Narcissus was overjoyed. He put his hand into the pool to take the nymph's hand – but at once the water rippled and the reflection of his lovely face was gone. Narcissus waited till the water was clear again, and then saw what he thought was the nymph once more smiling at him.

Poor Narcissus! He fell deeply in love with his own image, though he did not once guess that the nymph was only himself. He would not leave the pool, but day and night, by sunshine and moonlight, he entreated the nymph to come from the water and be his love. When he smiled, she smiled. When he looked sad, so did she. Echo came by and saw what was happening, and she grieved bitterly to see her prayer fulfilled in such a way.

Narcissus forgot to eat and drink – and on the fourth day he died. The gods, looking down on the beautiful youth, were sorry for him, and changed him into the lovely flower that bears his name. And still it loves to grow by pools where it can lean over and see its own lovely image.

As for Echo, she pined away in the mountains until she became nothing but a voice. You may still hear it, repeating your last words – and then we say, 'Hark! Listen to the echo!'

Littlefeet and the Thrush

A LONG time ago Littlefeet the Elf took up his paint-pots one springtime, and set out to paint all the spring flowers in their bright colours. His work was in Cuckoo Wood, and it was a long way away. Littlefeet asked a big bumble bee to carry him to the wood, and very soon he was there.

He set out all his pots, mixed his colours, and began to paint primroses, violets and celandines. He was a very good workman. By the time one o'clock came he was quite ready for his dinner.

'I'm so hungry I could almost eat my hat!' he sang. 'But I won't, because it's a nice new one. Now, where's my dinner?'

He looked round for the red handkerchief in which he always carried his dinner, neatly tied up – but, oh, dear me, he had forgotten to bring it with him! His dinner was sitting at home, miles away!

Littlefeet was dreadfully upset. Whatever was he to do?

'I must go without, I suppose,' said Littlefeet. 'But I'm sure I shall never last out till tea-time!'

Just then a large brown bird flew down beside the elf.

'Have you forgotten your dinner?' he asked. 'I'll go back and fetch it for you if you like!'

Off flew the thrush, and was back again with Littlefeet's dinner in a second. The elf was so grateful.

'What can I do for you in return for your kindness?' asked Littlefeet.

The thrush looked at all the bright paints set out on the grass.

'Could you paint me up a bit, so that I am a bit more colourful?' he asked. 'The robin has a red breast, the kingfisher is blue and green, the blackbird has a fine orange beak, but I am *so* dowdy. I have a brown back and a pale breast, and I feel I would like to wear a blue waistcoat, or something like that!'

'I'll see what colours I have over, and use them up on you!' promised the elf, and he set to work again on the flowers. But, do you know, there were so many that year in Cuckoo Wood that when the end of the day came the elf had used up all his greens and blues, yellows and reds, and all he had left was a pot of brown paint and a pot of black!

'Well, we must do the best we can with *this*,' he said to the disappointed thrush. 'What about a few nice black-brown speckles on your chest? Come here and I'll make you pretty!'

The thrush was pleased when he had finished, and all his friends admired him. *I* think he's very pretty, too, with his speckly, freckly breast – don't you?

The Animals' Band

A Tale From Grimm

ONCE a poor old donkey, a limping dog, a miserable cat and an unhappy cock all met together. They were sad because they were getting old and their masters did not want them any longer. 'Let us go to Bremen and join the town band,' said the donkey.

So off they all went; but they could not reach Bremen that night, for it was too far away. So they decided to take shelter in a wood. The donkey lay down under a tree with the dog, the cat climbed half-way, and the cock went to roost on the topmost bough. From there he had a good look round, and suddenly saw a house not far away.

'Cock-a-doodle-doo!' he cried to the others. 'I see a house near by. Let us go there, for maybe we shall get food.'

They set off for the house; but when they peered in at the window they saw a lot of robbers sitting round a table.

'Let us sing to them,' whispered the donkey. 'Then we will jump in at the window and ask for a meal.'

So the dog jumped up on the donkey's back, the cat leapt on to the dog's back, and the cock flew up and stood on the cat. Then the donkey brayed, the dog barked, the cat mewed, and the cock crowed. After that they all leapt in at the window. The robbers were terrified out of their lives. First they heard the terrible noise, and when the animals came leaping in they fled in panic. The animals were pleased, and ate all the things on the table. Then the donkey went to sleep in the yard, the dog lay down behind the door, the cat sat blinking by the dying fire, and the cock flew up to the rafters.

Presently one of the robbers came back to see if any one was there, for he thought that he and his friends had been too easily frightened. As he stumbled in at the door he looked towards the fire, and saw the cat's two gleaming eyes looking at him. He thought they were glowing embers, and decided to light a match from them so that he could see properly. He stuck a match into the cat's eyes, and she screeched and flew at him with her claws out, scratching his face. The robber turned in terror to run away, and as he passed the door the dog ran out from behind him and bit his leg. The man rushed out into the yard, and there fell over the donkey, who kicked him head over heels. Then the cock woke up and cried, 'Cock-a-doodle-doo, cock-a-doodle-doo!' and the robber tore back to his friends, trembling all over.

'Oh, oh,' he said. 'I went into the house, and there was a witch sitting by the fire with two gleaming eyes. She flew at me and tore my face. Then behind the door there was a man with a dagger, and he stabbed me in my leg! In the yard there lay a giant, and he kicked me head over heels. And up in the rafters sat a judge, who cried, "Bring the rogue to me!"'

All the robbers took to their heels and fled far away. The animals made the house their home, and lived very happily there. Indeed, some people declare that they are there to this very day!

The Complaining Tadpole

THERE was once a tadpole who thought he knew everything. He took no notice of what the bigger tadpoles told him, and when a grown frog said he was very silly to go so near the ducks on the pond he was angry.

'Pooh!' he said, rudely. 'What do you know about ducks, I should like to know! Why, I've been told that you've only been in this pond for five weeks, so you may be sure I shan't listen to *you*! *I've* been in the pond all my life!'

'Well, you're only three weeks old!' said the frog. 'Don't be silly. You want telling off. Hi, all you frogs, here is a tadpole that wants smacking!'

So all the frogs swam up, and the cheeky tadpole was told off. He was so angry! He swam off to the other tadpoles and told them all about it.

'What use are frogs!' he cried. 'Nasty, ill-natured things! Down with frogs! I shall go round and complain about them to everything in the pond.'

So he swam off alone, and went to where a minnow and a stickleback were chatting to one another.

'I want to complain about frogs!' he said. 'Down with frogs! Chase them out of the pond! Do you agree with me, stickleback and minnow?'

The fish laughed so much that they couldn't answer, and the tadpole swam away in disgust, wondering what they were laughing at. He saw a great black water-beetle, and wriggled up to him.

'Down with frogs!' he said. 'Chase them out of the pond! Do you agree with me, black water-beetle?'

The beetle stared at the tadpole in surprise, and then laughed till it could laugh no more, and had to rise to the top of the water to take more air in to breathe.

'Silly creature!' said the tadpole, and swam off to a newt. 'Down with frogs!' he said to the astonished newt. 'Chase them out of the pond! Do you agree with me, newt?'

The newt began to laugh, and swallowed a fly he was eating in such a hurry that it went down the wrong way and he began to choke.

'Stupid thing!' said the tadpole, and swam off

to a water-snail. 'Down with frogs!' he said. 'Chase them out of the pond! Do you agree with me, water-snail?'

'Don't be foolish!' said the snail, and began to laugh, so that bubbles of air escaped from his mouth and rose up to the top of the water in a silvery line.

'Why does every one laugh when I say, "Down with frogs!"?' cried the tadpole crossly. '*I* don't think it's funny!'

The water-snail laughed again. Then the newt, the black water-beetle, the minnow and the stickleback all came up and began to laugh too.

'We'll make you a promise, tadpole,' they said. 'If you come back in six weeks' time and say, "Down with frogs! Chase them out of the pond!" we'll do it. Now go away!'

'I'll be back in six weeks' time!' promised the tadpole, eagerly, and swam off, very much delighted. But when the six weeks were up, he *didn't* go back! And who can tell me why?

Brer Rabbit and the Meat

ONE time Brer Wolf and Brer Rabbit came across a fine piece of meat lying by the roadside.

'I'm the biggest, so I'll have the most,' said Brer Wolf. 'I'll carve myself my share and take it home, and you can have what's left.'

Well, Brer Rabbit didn't like the sound of that at all, but he didn't dare to argue with Brer Wolf. So he just sat by as if he didn't care a rap. Brer Wolf went on cutting and carving, and presently Brer Rabbit began to sniff hard.

'Brer Wolf!' he said. 'Does this meat smell all right to you?'

Brer Wolf didn't trouble to answer. He just went on cutting and carving. Then Brer Rabbit walked all round the meat, and he kicked it and prodded it.

'Brer Wolf,' he said, 'this meat feels mighty flabby to me. Do you think it's good?'

Brer Wolf heard every word, but he didn't pay any attention at all. He just went on cutting and carving, carving and cutting.

'Well, you can talk or not talk, just as you please,' said Brer Rabbit, 'but you'll be sorry for yourself soon.'

Then Brer Rabbit ran off, and came back with firewood and a dish of salt.

'What are you going to do?' asked Brer Wolf.

'What am I going to do?' said Brer Rabbit with a laugh. 'I'll tell you what I'm going to do. I'm just going to cook a bit of this meat and taste it to see if it *is* bad or not, because you don't suppose I'm going to bother to carry a great piece all the way home if it's bad, do you?'

With that he made a little fire, cut off a piece of the meat, salted it and cooked it over the flames. Then he tasted it. He nibbled it and he tasted it, he tasted it and he nibbled it till he had eaten a good piece. Then he went and sat a little way off as if he were waiting to see if anything would happen.

Brer Wolf went on cutting and carving, cutting and carving, but all the time he watched Brer Rabbit. Soon he saw him fling both hands up to his head and heard him groan terribly. Still, Brer Wolf cut and carved, and watched Brer Rabbit. Then Brer Rabbit swayed himself backwards and forwards and groaned again. Then he rolled on the ground and began to shout, 'Oh, my! Oh, my! The meat's poisoned!'

Brer Wolf stopped his cutting and carving and looked at Brer Rabbit in alarm.

'Run and fetch the doctor!' groaned Brer Rabbit. 'Run, Brer Wolf! I'm poisoned, I tell you, run, run!'

Brer Wolf dropped his knife, scared stiff, and ran for the doctor. As soon as he was out of sight Brer Rabbit jumped up and went to the meat. Bit by bit he carried it off to his home, and very soon he had it all safely in his larder. Then he sat down and laughed. You should have heard him!

As for old Brer Wolf, when he came back with the doctor Brer Rabbit was gone and so was the meat! Poor old Brer Wolf!

The Cock and the Fox

A Tale From Aesop's Fables

ONCE upon a time a cock flew up into a tree and began to crow. As he crowed loudly he saw a fox come running up. The fox was thin and very hungry-looking, and the cock thought that it would be better to stay in the tree till the fox had gone. 'Ho, Rooster,' said the fox. 'Come down here. I have great news for you!'

'What is that?' asked the cock.

'Listen,' said the fox. 'All the birds and animals have promised to live at peace one with another. There will no longer be war between us. The lamb may lie down with the wolf, and the bird may sleep side by side with the cat. Is not this good news?' The cock did not answer. He stood on his toes and strained his neck as if he were looking at something a great distance away.

'Do you not hear my good news?' asked the fox impatiently. 'Come down, Rooster, and let us go walking together and talk of my news. Fly down beside me.'

Still the cock did not answer, but seemed to be looking far away.

'What is it that you can see?' asked the fox, crossly.

'It is a pack of hounds, I think,' said the cock. 'In a moment we may hear them baying.'

When he heard what the cock said the fox started up in fright, and made as if he would go.

'What's the matter?' asked the cock, pretending to be surprised. 'Did you not say that all the animals are at peace? Why are you afraid of dogs, then? They will not hurt you.'

'N-n-no,' stammered the fox, not knowing what to say. 'B-b-ut you see, they may not have heard my news!' And with that he ran off as fast as his legs could carry him.

'Ha, ha!' shouted the cock after him. 'I quite understand you, Fox! Cock-a-doodle-doo! Cock-a-doodle-doo!'

The Slave of the Stone

TACKY was a small brownie, who was servant to the great magician Gloomy-one. Gloomy-one had a magic stone which, when he threw it into the air three times, brought to him a slave, who would do anything he wished.

Tacky thought it was wonderful. The slave would bring delicious meals out of the air, and could even make sacks of gold appear, merely by holding out his hand.

Now, one day the magician went out and forgot to take his magic stone with him. There it stood on the mantelshelf, and when Tacky came in to fetch the mats for beating, he saw it.

'O-oh!' said Tacky. 'I wonder if the slave would come for me!'

He took the stone, and threw it three times into the air. At once there was a loud crash, and there stood the slave of the stone, looking very angry indeed, to find that it was Tacky who had made him come and not the magician.

'What do you want me to do?' he asked, in a loud, booming voice.

'N-n-nothing,' said Tacky in a fright.

'Tell me something to do, quickly, or I will spirit you away with me!' cried the slave in a temper.

Well, do you suppose Tacky could think of anything to tell the slave to do? He stood there trembling, and racked his brains to think of a task.

'Be quick!' boomed the slave. Then Tacky remembered the dusty mats, and he spoke to the slave.

'Shake the mats well!' he commanded, in a very small voice. At once the slave caught up the mats and took them into the garden. He began to shake them, but so great was his strength that the shaking made a tremendous wind, and all the curtains of the house started flapping, and Tacky was blown flat on the ground.

'Stop! Stop!' cried Tacky. But the slave took no notice at all. He went on shaking and shaking the mats, and the wind blew bigger and bigger. The house started to rock from side to side, and the trees bent almost to the ground. Tacky was blown straight up into the air, and goodness knows where he would have gone to if he hadn't managed to catch hold of a chimney and hold on tight!

The wind blew bigger still, for the slave shook the mats more powerfully than ever, pleased to see the mischief he was doing. Tacky felt quite sure that the whole house would be blown away – and then, to his great joy, he saw the magician coming home down the street, staring in astonishment to see his house rocking from side to side and Tacky holding on to a chimney. He saw in a moment what had happened, and called out commandingly to the slave:

'Stop, O slave of the stone! You are in disgrace! Disappear! Fly! Vanish!'

The slave disappeared into the air. The wind died down. Tacky was smacked, and ran howling to the kitchen.

'O-oh!' he said. 'I'll never meddle with magic again! No, I never will!' And I don't suppose he ever did.

The Tale of the Admiral

ONCE, when Bray the Donkey was standing by the field gate, he heard the farmer's wife say: 'Look! There's a red admiral coming down the lane!'

Bray pricked up his ears and ran to Daisy the Cow. 'I say, what do you think?' he cried. 'There's an admiral coming down the lane! Do you know what an admiral is? He's a marvellous sailor, very grand indeed. I know, because my mother belonged to one, and he had ever so many ships of his own. He's sure to come and see us all, so hurry up and make yourself smart.'

'I must tell Captain the Horse,' said Daisy, and she ran to where he was standing in the shade of a tree. 'Make yourself smart!' she said. 'A great admiral is coming to see us!'

'My gracious!' said Captain, swishing his tail. 'What an honour, to be sure! I must go and tell Tubby the Pig!' So he galloped to where Tubby was rolling in her sty.

'Make yourself smart!' he said. 'A great admiral is coming to see us!'

'Pigs and whistles!' cried Tubby. 'I never heard of such a thing! I must go and tell Waddle the Duck!' So she went to where Waddle was swimming on the pond.

'Make yourself smart!' she cried. 'A great admiral is coming to see us!'

'Did you ever hear the like!' quacked Waddle. 'I must go and tell the farmer's wife!' So she waddled off to tell the farmer's wife, who was most astonished to hear such news.

'Who told you?' she asked.

'Tubby the Pig,' said Waddle. So they went to Tubby the Pig and asked who had told her.

'Captain the Horse,' answered Tubby. So they went to Captain and asked who had told *him*.

'Daisy the Cow!' said Captain. So they went to Daisy and asked who had told *her*.

'Bray the Donkey!' said Daisy. So they went to Bray and asked who had told *him*.

'Why, I heard the farmer's wife say so herself!' cried Bray, looking at her in great astonishment. 'You said, "Look! There's a red admiral coming down the lane!" Didn't you now, Mistress?'

Then the farmer's wife began to laugh and laugh as if she would never stop. At last she dried her eyes and took all the animals to the lane. She looked up and down, and then pointed to a sunny wall.

'There's the red admiral!' she said, and all the animals looked and looked.

And what did they see? Nothing but a lovely red butterfly, opening and shutting his wings in the sun!

'Silly donkey!' said all the animals to Bray, and they walked off holding their heads high in the air!

Brer Wolf's Trick

ONE day Brer Wolf told Brer Fox that he had thought of a mighty fine plan to catch Brer Rabbit.

'You lie on your bed and pretend you're dead,' he said to Brer Fox. 'Then I'll go round to Brer Rabbit and tell him. He'll come to see if you are, for sure, and as soon as he gets into the room, you up and catch him! Then we'll have him for dinner!'

Brer Fox agreed, and Brer Wolf went round to Brer Rabbit's. He knocked at the door, blim-blam, blim-blam.

'Who's there?' said Brer Rabbit.

'Friend,' said Brer Wolf.

'Too many friends spoil my dinner,' said Brer Rabbit. 'Which one's this?'

'I bring bad news,' said Brer Wolf.

'Bad news is soon told,' said Brer Rabbit, coming to the window.

'Brer Fox is dead,' said Brer Wolf, pretending to wipe his eyes.

'Why haven't you got a black coat on, then?'

asked Brer Rabbit.

'I'm just going after it now,' said Brer Wolf. 'I only came to tell you the news.' And with that he loped off.

Brer Rabbit sat down and scratched his head, and by and by he made up his mind to go round by Brer Fox's house to see if the news was true. Up he jumped, and out he went. When he got near to the house it looked sort of lonesome, so Brer Rabbit went closer. Still he saw nobody stirring, so he crept up to the door and looked in. Then he saw Brer Fox lying on his bed as still as anything.

Then Brer Rabbit made as if he were talking to himself.

'Nobody here to look after poor dead Brer Fox!' he said. 'Not even Brer Turkey-Buzzard. I hope Brer Fox isn't dead, but I expect he is. Even Brer Wolf's gone and left him. It's a busy time with me, but I'll sit by him. He looks as if he's dead, yet he mayn't be. When any one goes to see dead foxes, dead foxes always kick up their hind leg and shout, "Wahoo!"'

Brer Fox stayed still. Brer Rabbit looked hard at him, but he didn't go in at the door. He just peeped round it, and began talking to himself more loudly still.

'This is mighty funny. Brer Fox *looks* as if he's dead, but he doesn't *act* as if he is. Dead foxes always kick up their hind leg and shout, "Wahoo!" when any one comes to see them,' said Brer Rabbit.

Sure enough, Brer Fox suddenly lifted up his hind leg and yelled out, 'Wahoo!' Brer Rabbit gave a big grin and tore out of the house as if the dogs were after him! On his way home he met Brer Wolf, who was most surprised to see him, for he thought surely Brer Fox would have caught him.

'Hey-ho, Brer Wolf!' said Brer Rabbit. 'Brer Fox has come alive again. He was shouting and kicking like anything when I left him!' And off he skipped as lively as a blackbird.

The Lark and the Cornfield

A Tale From Aesop's Fables

ONCE upon a time there were two larks. It was springtime and they were very happy. They flew up into the blue sky every morning, and sang till they could sing no more.

They made a nest of dry grass in a field of young corn. They placed it in the big footprint of a cart-horse, and they loved it, for it was to be the cradle for their young ones.

The mother lark laid four mottled, brown eggs in her nest, and then waited patiently for them to hatch. At last the shells broke, and out came the babes.

'We are safe here!' said the mother lark. 'The green corn has grown so high that our nest is hidden. No one can see us; we are safe, safe, safe!'

'Wait till the reapers come!' said the listening rabbit. 'They will cut down the corn and your nest will be destroyed.'

'The reapers do not come till the corn is ripe

and golden,' sang the mother lark. 'By that time my babies will be ready to fly with me.'

But the corn ripened quickly that year. The mother lark grew anxious, for her babies were not yet old enough to fly.

'Watch well every day when I am away from you,' she said to her little brood. 'Tell me all you hear, when I come back.'

When she returned the young larks were in a terrible fright. 'Mother!' they cried, 'we are lost! The farmer passed by today, and said he is going to call in the neighbours to reap our field.'

'That is good,' said the mother lark. 'If he trusts to his neighbours the work will never be done!'

Next morning the farmer came again, and the little larks listened in fear.

'I must send for my brothers and nephews,' he said. 'We will begin reaping tomorrow.'

When the frightened baby larks told their mother this she said: 'That is good. His relations are busy with their own work, so we need not fear that our corn will be cut yet.'

Four days later the farmer came again, and the mother lark flew near by to hear what he was saying.

'I really must start reaping this field myself

tomorrow,' he said. Then the lark flew to her young ones, and bade them make ready to fly.

'We must go!' she said. '*For when a man says that he will do his work himself it is sure to be done!*'

Then up rose all the larks together, and flew far away to a place of safety.

Tuppeny and the Pink Plums

ONCE upon a time Tuppeny the elf wanted to go out. It was raining, but he wasn't at all sad to see the big drops, because he had new goloshes, a new macintosh, a new sou'wester, and a beautiful, brand-new umbrella.

'Ha!' said Tuppeny, 'I'll put them all on!'

He did so, and out he went into the rain and kept as dry as could be. He hadn't gone very far before he met Raggedy the Pixie sheltering under a bush. Raggedy had on an old tunic and nothing else, and he was very wet indeed. Didn't his little eyes gleam when he saw Tuppeny!

'Hallo, Raggedy,' said Tuppeny. 'How are you this morning?'

'Oh,' said Raggedy, 'I'm most annoyed with this rain. I was just on my way to a beautiful tree full of pink plums when it started to pour – and I got so wet that I had to shelter. And now I'm afraid, if the rain doesn't stop, some one else will find those pink plums and they'll all be gone before I can get them.'

'Tell me where they are and I'll go and pick some,' said Tuppeny.

'Oh, it's too difficult to tell you exactly where the tree is,' said Raggedy. 'But see, Tuppeny, if you'll lend me your macintosh I could easily go and get enough for us both.'

Tuppeny stripped off his macintosh and Raggedy put it on. Then, leaving Tuppeny under the bush, he ran off. But soon he was back again.

'There are such a lot of puddles,' he said. 'Could you lend me your goloshes, too?' So Tuppeny lent him his goloshes, and once more he ran off. But in a minute he was back again.

'Every time I look up at the tree to see just where the plums are the raindrops dash into my eyes,' he said. 'Could you lend me your sou'wester too, Tuppeny?'

So Tuppeny lent him his sou'wester, and off ran Raggedy again. When he came back for the third time Tuppeny quite expected to see his hands full of plums. But no, he hadn't a single one.

'Oh, Tuppeny,' he said, 'I can't reach *any* of the plums. Could you lend me your umbrella to knock some down?'

So Tuppeny lent him his beautiful brand-new umbrella, and Raggedy ran off.

But this time he didn't come back. Tuppeny waited and waited and waited, but still Raggedy didn't come back. The rain stopped and the sun came out and still Raggedy didn't come. What *could* have happened to him? The elf crept out from under the bush and started down the lane. Soon he met a pedlar, and he asked him if he had seen a tree of pink plums.

'Pink plums!' said the pedlar, and laughed loudly. 'No! And there isn't a tree of pink plums this side of Fairyland, let me tell you – but I've seen something else, and that's Raggedy the pixie, all rigged out in new goloshes, macintosh, and sou'wester and carrying a beautiful, brand-new umbrella – and he's caught the train for Dreamland in a mighty hurry!'

Then Tuppeny went red with rage and white with grief, for he knew that never again would he see any of his lovely rain-clothes: and, of course, he didn't.

Tippitty Tells a Tale

TIPPITTY the Green Elf hopped in at the school window one morning to see what the children were doing. They were painting white snowdrops on black paper, and she thought they were very good.

'I can tell you something that you don't know about snowdrops!' she said, with a chuckle. 'Go on painting and listen while I tell you.

'Well, many, many years ago, before your great-great-grandmothers were born, all the snowdrops held their white heads upright as the primroses do. None of them drooped at all. Didn't you know that, girls and boys? Ah, you don't know everything, even though you learn such a lot!

'One night there was a party in Princess Miranda's garden, and all the Green Elves were invited. They were most excited, and they all made themselves new green dresses and tunics. The party was on the first of February, and was at twelve o'clock at night.

'Just as midnight struck we all came trooping into the garden, dozens of us. The grass was nice and green, and all round about stood the snowdrops, their heads well up in the air, for they always thought quite a lot of themselves, being one of the very first flowers brave enough to come out.

'The party was in full swing, and we were all enjoying ourselves very much indeed, when a dreadful thing happened. A visitor came to the garden, and who do you think he was?

'He was a tall thin man, dressed in white from top to toe, and his breath was like an icy wind. Guess his name? Yes, you're right, it was that horrid fellow Jack Frost! I know he does a lot of good to the farmers, because he breaks up their fields for them, but we Green Elves hate him. He pinches our fingers and toes, and makes us shiver from head to foot!

'Of course, he quite spoilt the party, for it was much too cold to go on with it – and the worst of it was, when the Princess Miranda invited all her guests into the palace to stay for the night, she quite forget about us. We are very, very small, you see, and I don't expect she noticed us much. We didn't know *what* to do! Jack Frost had made all the grass silvery with frost, so we couldn't lie there. The trees had no leaves, so we couldn't go there.

'So what do you think we did? We ran to the snowdrops and climbed into the very middle of them, begging them to close their outside petals over us for blankets. They did as we asked, and we slept there comfortably all night through.

'But in the morning, when the Princess Miranda walked in her garden, she cried out in surprise at the sight of her snowdrops. "Why, they're all drooping their heads!" she said. And so they were, because our weight had bent them down! We jumped out and said good morning, and she *was* astonished! "I like my snowdrops *much* better with drooping heads!" she said. "Please stay like that." So they did.

'And do you know, each year when the new snowdrops shoot up, all with heads held straight up, we Green Elves creep into them and make them droop with our weight. What? You don't believe me? I'll prove it to you! Pick up the snowdrops you are painting and look inside them. Do you see the green streaks on the white? Well, that's where our dresses rubbed! Good-bye!'

And isn't it strange, children – the snowdrops certainly *have* got green streaks inside!

Brer Rabbit's Cow

HAVE you heard this tale of wicked Brer Rabbit?

One day Brer Wolf was coming home from fishing, with a string of fish across his shoulder. Suddenly old Miss Partridge hopped out of the bushes, and fluttered along right under Brer Wolf's nose. 'Ho, ho!' said Brer Wolf. 'Her nest is somewhere near. I'll find it.'

So he put down his fishes, and went to look. About that time Brer Rabbit happened along. There were the fishes and there was Brer Rabbit – but neither of them stayed there long, and when Brer Wolf came back, his string of fishes was nowhere to be seen.

He sat down and scratched his head, and after a bit it came into his mind that Brer Rabbit must have been along that way. So he set out for Brer Rabbit's house, and hailed him. But Brer Rabbit said he didn't know anything about strings of fishes. Brer Wolf vowed he did, and they argued it up and down till Brer Rabbit said, 'Well, if

I've got those fishes of yours, you can go and kill my best cow!'

He didn't reckon Brer Wolf would take him at his word, but that's just what he did. Off he went to the meadow to kill Brer Rabbit's best cow.

Well, Brer Rabbit felt mighty bad when he thought he was going to lose his cow, but he laid his plans, and told his children that he wouldn't lose his beef, they'd see! So he raced up to Brer Wolf, lippitty-clippitty, and told him that the policeman was coming. 'You run and hide,' he said, 'and I'll stay here and take care of the cow till you get back.'

Brer Wolf shot into the bushes, for he was afraid of the policeman. As soon as he was gone, Brer Rabbit killed his cow, salted the hide down, cut up the meat and stowed it away in his smoke-house. Then he took the cow-tail and stuck the end of it in the ground.

'Run, run, Brer Wolf!' he shouted. 'Run, run! Your cow's going into the ground!'

When old Brer Wolf got there, he saw Brer Rabbit holding on to the cow-tail, as if he was keeping the cow from going into the ground. Brer Wolf caught hold too, and after he had given a pull or two, out came the tail!

'There,' said Brer Rabbit, 'you've pulled the tail off, and your cow's gone!'

But Brer Wolf wasn't going to give up. He got a spade, a pick-axe and a shovel, and he dug for that cow till he could dig no more. Old Brer Rabbit sat up there in his front porch, smoking a cigar, and every time Brer Wolf struck his pick-axe into the clay, Brer Rabbit giggled to his children:

'He diggy, diggy, diggy, but there's no meat there! He diggy, diggy, diggy, but there's no meat there!'

And all the time he knew that the cow was turned into beef in his smoke-house, and he and his children were eating fried beef and onions whenever they felt hungry.

Old Brer Wolf never found that cow – but I'm not surprised at that, are you?

The Chocolate Rabbit

IN Mother Buttercup's shop there were lots of Easter eggs, marzipan chickens and chocolate rabbits. In the middle of the window sat the biggest rabbit of all. He was very fine indeed, and was made of chocolate from his tail to his long ears.

He was a very proud rabbit, and thought he was meant for great things. All the children who came by admired him, and that made him vainer than ever – so you can guess what a shock it was for him when the yellow chicken next to him told him that he was made to be eaten!

'*Eaten!*' said the rabbit in horror. '*Eaten!* I never heard of such a thing! Why, I mean to be king of the rabbits before the year is out!'

Now just at that minute a little girl came into the shop to buy him. Mother Buttercup lifted him out of the window and popped him into a paper bag – but the rabbit nibbled a hole in it, leapt to the floor, and was out of the door in a twinkling!

'Come back, come back!' shouted the little girl. 'I want you!'

But the rabbit didn't stop. Not he! *He* wasn't going to be eaten! He raced down the street, and ran between the legs of a big brown dog.

'Come back, come back!' shouted the dog, sniffing the smell of chocolate. 'I want you!'

But the rabbit didn't stop. Not he! *He* wasn't going to be eaten! He ran round the corner, jumped over a wall, and landed right on top of a Persian cat, who was asleep in the sun. The cat woke up with a jump, and as soon as she saw that the rabbit was made of chocolate, she shouted after him.

'Come back! Come back! I want you!'

But the rabbit didn't stop. Not he! *He* wasn't going to be eaten. He ran straight on, and suddenly, splash! he fell into a pond. He struggled out, dripping wet, and oh, how cold he felt! He began to shiver and shake, and longed to get warm.

Very soon he came to where a group of children were making a picnic fire in a wood. The rabbit crept close up to the flames and sat down to warm himself.

'Who are you, little rabbit?' asked the children in surprise.

'I'm a chocolate rabbit, but I'm *not* going to be eaten!' said the rabbit, fiercely. 'Don't come near me! I fell into a pond, and now I want to get warm. If you come near me, I'll bite you!'

'Let's go and find mother and tell her about this funny rabbit,' said the children, half-afraid to go near. So they went to find their mother. The rabbit crept nearer and nearer to the fire. Suddenly he began to feel sleepy. His head drooped forward and his eyes closed.

'I *won't* be eaten! I *won't* be eaten!' he said dreamily – and that was the last he said – for suddenly the heat of the fire melted him, and in a moment there was no rabbit left, only a pool of brown chocolate on the ground.

And when the children came back with their mother, what did they see? Nothing but a big brown dog and a Persian cat licking something by the fire!

The Golden Pennies

SNOOKY the Gnome was passing Witch Tiptap's house one evening, when she came out of her back door and beckoned to him.

'I want a new broomstick to ride on,' she said. 'Go and cut me one from the hedgerows, Snooky.'

'How much will you pay me?' asked Snooky.

'A piece of gold,' said Tiptap. So Snooky ran gladly to the hedgerow, and cut a fine broomstick. He trimmed it and smoothed it, and then took it to Tiptap. But no sooner had she got it in her hand than she slammed her door and wouldn't hear of giving Snooky his piece of gold at all.

Snooky was angry. He peeped here and he peeped there, trying to see where Witch Tiptap kept her gold. And at last, in the corner of an old shed, he found a sackful of golden pennies!

'Ho, ho!' said Snooky, greedily. 'Look at this! I'll just hoist the whole sack on my shoulder and take it away! That will serve Tiptap right for not giving me the one piece of gold she promised me!'

With that he lifted the heavy sack on his shoulder and off he went with it. Night was falling, and nobody saw Snooky running down the street.

'I'd better not go to my cottage,' he said. 'If I do the witch will soon find me there. No! With all this gold I'll run right away into the land of humans, and there I'll live as rich as can be in the heart of a wood!'

So off he went, and soon came to our world. For miles and miles he wandered all over the countryside, trying to find a nice place for his new home – and suddenly he noticed a strange thing! The sack was no longer heavy, but as light as could be!

Snooky put it down and looked at it, and, oh, my! it had a hole in the bottom, and one by one, the golden pennies had dropped out in the fields, the hedges, and along the roadsides!

'There's only one left!' wept Snooky. 'And, oh! the witch will be able to follow me by the track of the shining pennies. Whatever shall I do? I'd better ask the first pixie I see to help me.'

So he did – and the pixie said that for a golden

penny she would make a spell that would turn all the dropped gold into yellow flowers. Then the witch wouldn't be able to see the gold, and couldn't catch Snooky. In a trice she waved her wand and muttered a string of strange words. What happened Snooky couldn't see, for it was dark. He paid the pixie the last golden penny and then sadly curled himself up in a hollow tree for the night.

But in the morning, what a sight all over our countryside! Round yellow flowers, as bright as the sun and as round as the golden pennies, gleamed everywhere.

'Where *did* they come from?' cried the children. 'Aren't they beautiful?'

What were they? Do you know? Yes, you are right! They were golden dandelions!

The Birthday Cake

ONCE upon a time Pom-Pom the Pixie found eleven eggs hidden in one corner of his barn. He hadn't kept hens for some time, so he knew they must be very old eggs. He was a mean person, and a horrid idea came into his head.

'I'll send them to the Bee-Woman,' he thought. 'She'll think I have made her a lovely present, and perhaps she'll give me some of her new honey.'

So he put them into a basket and sent them to the Bee-Woman.

'Dear, dear!' she said, when she had got them. 'Now I really don't want any more eggs today, I've just bought twelve. I know! I'll send them to the Balloon Man! He's been ill, and will be glad of them!'

So she sent them across to the Balloon Man. When he saw them, he sighed.

'Now, what a pity!' he said. 'This is the third lot of eggs I have had sent me today! Well, well, I shall never be able to eat them all, that's certain – so I'll send them to my poor old Aunt Toppytoes. I'm sure she'll be very glad of them, indeed.'

So he sent them to his Aunt Toppytoes, and she was so surprised to get a present.

'But, oh, it's eggs!' she said. 'And the doctor says I mustn't eat a single egg for a month. So I'd better think of some one to send them to. I know! I'll send them to Chippy the Elf. He's fond of making cakes, and these will come in handy for his baking day!'

So the eggs were sent to Chippy. He was delighted with them. 'I'll make a fine birthday cake for Pom-Pom!' he decided. 'It's his birthday tomorrow, and it will be a lovely present for him. He's having a party, so it will come in very useful.'

Now Chippy had got a cold, so he didn't smell how bad the eggs were when he broke them and beat them into his flour. He made a beautiful cake, and iced it all over, and then wrote 'A HAPPY BIRTHDAY' on it. When Pom-Pom saw it he was very joyful.

'It shall be for my party!' he said. 'Thank you very much, Chippy.'

But, oh, dear! What a dreadful cake that was when it came to be eaten. Everybody made a face and choked terribly.

'You made it of bad eggs,' said Pom-Pom to Chippy, in a very cross voice.

'I got the eggs from Mrs Toppytoes,' said Chippy. '*Were* they bad, Mrs Toppytoes?'

'I don't know,' said Aunt Toppytoes. '*I* got them from the Balloon Man. *Were* they bad, Balloon Man?'

'I don't know,' said the Balloon Man. '*I* got them from the Bee Woman. *Were* they bad, Bee-Woman?'

'I don't know,' she said. '*I* got them from Pom-Pom himself. If they were bad, he has spoilt his own birthday cake, and it serves him right!'

And I think it did, don't you?

Sandy and the Moon

ONE bright night Sandy, the puppy, saw the moon sailing in the sky, and it frightened him.

'What's that?' he asked Bobs, the dog.

'The moon,' said Bobs. 'Can you see him looking at you? There's a man in the moon, you know, Sandy. Be careful that he doesn't eat you!'

'He'd better be careful I don't eat *him*!' said Sandy, fiercely. 'Ho, Moon? Do you see my sharp teeth? Be careful, or I will eat you!'

The moon took no notice at all, but went on sailing swiftly through the clouds. Every time it came out from behind them Sandy thought that the moon was staring at him, and he grew very angry.

'Go away!' he barked. 'You staring moon, how dare you look at me like that?'

He barked and barked, he growled in his throat, and he snarled and snapped – but still the moon sailed in the sky and was as bright as ever. At last Sandy's neck ached with looking upwards, and he went into his kennel to lie down.

He hadn't been there very long before his Mistress came down the path and whistled softly. 'Ho, Bobs, ho, Sandy? What about a walk on this lovely night?'

Out rushed both the dogs and danced round their mistress. Then down the lane they went, barking and jumping. Sandy had forgotten all about the moon – until suddenly he came to a large puddle. And there, shining in the middle of it, was the silver moon! It looked up at Sandy and it seemed to laugh at him. 'Here I am again!' it said.

'Ha!' wuffed Sandy, in excitement. 'You've got into that puddle, have you! All right! I'll have you now!'

He scraped and scraped at the puddle to get the moon out, but he couldn't get it. It broke up into little bits, but it joined itself together again in a few moments, and laughed at Sandy.

'I'll get you *somehow*!' growled Sandy. 'I know! I'll drink the puddle, and find you at the bottom of it. Then I'll chew you into bits!'

So he began to drink the puddle. It was a large one, but Sandy wouldn't give up. He drank and drank, and his little body swelled up like a balloon. At last he had drunk it all up, and he looked for the moon at the bottom – but it wasn't there!

Just then his mistress came back with Bobs, and she looked at him in surprise. 'Whatever have you drunk all that puddle for?' she asked. 'You *must* have been thirsty, Sandy.'

'The moon was in there,' said Sandy, 'so I drank the water to get at it – but oh, Mistress, the moon isn't there now, so I must have drunk it! Oh, it's giving me such a pain! Oh, I've got the moon inside me!'

Then Bobs laughed till his tail nearly fell off. 'Look up into the sky!' he said, and Sandy looked. There was the moon, sailing quietly between the clouds. 'Well, however did it get back there?' cried Sandy in amazement – and he doesn't know to this very day!

The Little Christmas Tree

THERE was once a little fir-tree that hated Christmas time. When it saw the snow coming it shivered and shook from top to toe.

'What's the matter?' asked a rabbit who had come out to nibble at the bark of a big tree near by.

'It's Christmas,' said the fir-tree. 'It may mean nothing to you, rabbit, but it frightens me. You see, I'm big enough now to be a real proper Christmas tree at a party. I shall be pulled up by my roots, and hung up in a shop. I shall be bought and carried home. I shall have sharp spikes stuck into my tender branches when I am decorated, and, worse than that, candles will be lighted all over me. I shall be burnt, I know I shall!'

'Well, you're a funny sort of tree,' said the rabbit, in surprise. 'Most fir-trees are very proud to amuse the children.'

Just then a man came by with a spade. When he saw the little fir-tree he dug it up and put it into a cart. Then he carried it away to the nearest town. It trembled all the way, for it knew that its time had come. Soon it was hung outside a shop, and presently a little girl came to buy it.

'Now I shall have sharp spikes set into my branches,' groaned the tree, 'and candles will burn me.'

The little girl carried the tree home and planted it in a round bed in the garden. The fir-tree was so surprised, for it had thought it would be put into a tub. 'I shan't be a Christmas tree after all!' it thought.

But it was. The little girl decorated it next day, and hung all kinds of presents on it – but what funny presents they were! The tree couldn't understand them at all. There were twelve bits of coconut, eight biscuits, ten crusts of bread, two strings of monkey-nuts twisted round and round its branches, six pieces of suet and five sprays of millet seed hung all around it!

'Well, whatever is all this for?' wondered the tree in astonishment. He soon knew on Christmas morning, for there came such a rustle and flutter of wings, such a twitter and chirping! Down flew all the birds in the garden and perched in the branches of the little fir-tree.

Robins and sparrows, thrushes and blackbirds, starlings and tits, finches and hedge-sparrows, they all came and pecked eagerly at the presents on his branches.

'You're a birds' Christmas-tree!' cried a big thrush to the little tree. 'You're put out here for us! And every Christmas you'll be decorated like this, and in between times you'll grow bigger and bigger in the garden! Aren't you happy?'

'I should think I am!' cried the fir-tree, and you should have heard his branches rustle from top to toe!

Mister Sh!

THERE was once a little girl whose name was Sheila. She went to school every day and loved it – but she *was* bad at spelling. Her dictation was simply dreadful.

One day her teacher was telling the class that when the letters S and H were put together they said 'Sh!' just like the noise Mother made when the baby was asleep.

'Sheila's name says "Sh!" at the beginning,' said Peter.

'And my shoes say "Sh!" at the beginning,' said Dorothy.

'So they do,' said the teacher. 'Well now, listen, all of you. For homework you must make me out a list of ten words all beginning with "Sh!". That will be quite easy, and we'll see who has the best list tomorrow morning.'

Well, will you believe it, when Sheila got home and sat down after tea to do her homework, she couldn't think of any more words at all – not a single one! Soon she began to cry, and her mother came to see what was the matter.

'I can't do my homework, Mummy,' said Sheila. 'But you mustn't help me, because my teacher says that's not fair.'

'Never mind, dear,' said her mother. 'Go out and play a little while. Perhaps you'll be able to do it afterwards.'

So out went Sheila into the garden – and to her great surprise she saw some one else there too! It was the queerest little fat man she had ever seen, no taller than she was herself. On his tunic was sewn the letter S – and when he turned round Sheila saw that the letter H was on his back.

'Who are you?' she asked in astonishment.

'I'm Mister Sh!' he said, beaming all over his face, and he held out his right hand. 'Shake!' he said, and Sheila shook hands solemnly.

Then Mister Sh brought out a bag of peppermints and divided them between Sheila and himself. 'Share!' he said, and they both ate them all up.

'I haven't done my homework yet,' said Sheila.

'Shocking!' said the little man, pretending to look shocked. 'Shameful!'

Just at that moment it began to rain, and

Mister Sh sneezed. 'A sharp shower!' he said, pointing to the rain. 'Shall we shelter in the shed?'

They scampered to the shed and sat down there. Sheila took out her homework book and tried to think hard. Mister Sh came over beside her.

'Show me,' he said. Sheila showed him the empty page.

'Shirker!' said the little man, pointing his finger at her.

'I'm *not* a shirker,' said Sheila, crossly. 'I've been trying hard to do my homework. You just see if *you* can do it, Mister Clever!'

'Shan't, shan't, shan't!' shouted Mister Sh, and, before Sheila's very eyes, he vanished.

And do you know, when Sheila began to think, she found that Mister Sh had done all her homework for her! All she had to do was to write it down. Could *you* write it down too? Read the story again and try!

Old Brer Rabbit, He's a Good Fisherman!

ONE day, when Brer Rabbit, Brer Fox, Brer Coon and Brer Bear were clearing a piece of ground for planting, Brer Rabbit got tired. So he called out that he had run a thorn into his hand, and off he slipped to find some place where he could rest.

Soon he came to a well and looked down it. It had two buckets on a rope. One bucket was at the top and the other at the bottom. 'That looks cool!' said Brer Rabbit. 'I'll jump in this bucket and have a nap.'

So in he jumped – but his weight made the bucket go down the well, and the empty bucket came to the top instead. Brer Rabbit was mighty scared when he felt his bucket going down. When it reached the water and stopped there he sat as still as still, for he was afraid to move in case the bucket dropped a little farther and filled with water.

Now Brer Fox always kept one eye on Brer

Rabbit, and when he saw him running off he followed him. He was mighty surprised to see him jump into the well-bucket and go down the well.

'Ho!' thought Brer Fox, 'old Brer Rabbit keeps his gold down there!'

He ran to the well and peeped over the side, and didn't he get a surprise when he saw Brer Rabbit sitting in the bucket at the bottom!

'Hey-ho, Brer Rabbit!' shouted Brer Fox. 'Who are you visiting down there?'

'Oh, I'm just a-fishing,' said cunning old Brer Rabbit. 'I just said to myself that I'd surprise you all with some fishes for dinner, and so here I am and here are the fishes.'

'Are there many down there?' asked Brer Fox.

'Lots of them,' said Brer Rabbit. 'Come down and help me catch them, Brer Fox.'

'But how am I going to get down, Brer Rabbit?' asked Brer Fox.

'Oh, jump into the bucket at the top there, Brer Fox,' said Brer Rabbit.

Well, Brer Rabbit talked so happily and sweetly that Brer Fox jumped straight into the bucket and down he went – and his weight pulled Brer Rabbit up! When the two buckets passed one another, Brer Rabbit sang out:

> Good-bye, Brer Fox, take care of your
>   clothes!
> For this is the way the old world goes:
> Some go up and some go down,
> You'll get to the bottom all safe and sound!

As soon as Brer Rabbit got to the top he jumped out of his bucket and ran for the folk who owned the well, telling them that Brer Fox was down there muddying up their drinking water. Then he rushed back to the well and shouted:

> Here comes a man with a great big gun,
> When he hauls you up, you jump and run!

And that's just what Brer Fox did when the angry man hauled up the bucket, and in a short time Brer Rabbit and Brer Fox were back at work with the others – but none of them could think *why* Brer Rabbit kept laughing!

Chip, the Guinea Pig

CHIP was a pretty little guinea-pig, and he belonged to Philip, who was very proud of him. Chip had won a silver medal at a guinea-pig show, and it hung just outside his cage for all the world to see. He was very pleased about it.

One day Chip had a dreadful fright. A friend of Philip's came to see him, and as she was peeping into the cage the little girl said a strange thing.

'If you hold your guinea-pig up by his tail his eyes will drop out!' she said.

'Don't be silly,' said Philip, and took her away. But Chip heard what the little girl had said and he was in a fearful fright. He shook like a jelly, and wondered whatever he would do if some one held him up by his tail one day and his eyes dropped out.

'I'd better have my tail cut off!' he thought. 'Then no one can do such a dreadful thing to me. Yes, that's a fine idea! I'll have my tail cut right off!'

That night he slipped the catch of his cage and scampered out into the darkness. He went straight to Whiskers, the grey rabbit, and spoke to him.

'Please, Whiskers, cut off my tail,' he said.

Whiskers stared at Chip, and then he shook his head. 'I'm sorry,' he said, 'my scissors aren't sharp enough.'

'Then I'll go and ask Snap the Fox,' said Chip. 'Perhaps he can bite it off with his sharp teeth.'

He ran off to Snap's den, and as he went he heard Whiskers laughing, but he couldn't *think* why. He begged Snap to bite off his tail – but the fox shook his head.

'I'm sorry, but I've got toothache,' he said. 'So I can't bite very well today, Chip.'

'Then I'll go and ask Hoppy the Brownie,' said Chip. 'Perhaps he'll cut it off with his knife.'

He ran off to Hoppy's, and as he went he heard Snap laughing, but he couldn't *think* why. He begged Hoppy to cut off his tail – and the brownie looked at him hard.

'What will you give me if I do?' he asked. 'It would be very difficult to cut off your tail, Chip.'

'Well, I've only got one thing that belongs to me, and that's the silver medal hanging outside my cage,' said Chip.

'Give me that, and I'll do what you want,' said Hoppy. So Chip ran back and fetched his lovely medal. Hoppy took it, and then found a large bread-knife. He swished it through the air behind Chip. 'There!' he said. 'Your tail's off! Now hurry home quickly.'

Chip ran off happily, and as he went he heard Hoppy laughing, but he couldn't *think* why. Anyway, nobody could lift him up by his tail now, to make his eyes drop out!

Next day Chip told Philip what had happened to his silver medal – and Philip *was* cross.

'Oh, you little silly!' he cried. 'Don't you know that guinea-pigs never have tails! You didn't have one at all, and Hoppy only pretended to cut it off, so that he might get your medal! Oh, you *are* a silly! Nobody could make your eyes drop out by holding you up by your tail – because you didn't have one!'

Poor Chip! He knew why every one had laughed at him then. Did *you* know why?

The Lazy Rook

ROOKERY Nook was a great collection of rooks' nests high up in the trees near the old church. There were quite a hundred nests built of big and little twigs. In the new year the rooks used to come and have a look at their old nests, and decide when they would rebuild them for the springtime.

One year spring was early, and the rooks started to build their nests in February. The old rooks took the old nests, which only needed repairing and strengthening, and the young rooks were told to build new nests.

'You'll find plenty of twigs in the wood not far away,' the old rooks said. 'Look on the ground and you will see where the winter gales have thrown branches down from the trees.'

So the young rooks went to see. Among them was Caw-caw, a strong young fellow whose feathers shone as if they had been polished. He found some twigs and flew back to the branch on which he had chosen to build his nest. He arranged his twigs nicely, and then flew back for some more. But when he had done this for some time he began to get tired of it.

He was a lazy fellow, and he groaned when he thought of what a long time it would take him to search for enough twigs to build the whole of his big nest. He looked round, and near by he saw the half-finished nest of another rook. At the top of it were two fine strong twigs – just the kind that Caw-caw wanted to use next. So he hopped over to the nest, and when next its owner was away he took the two twigs and used them for his own nest.

Then he stole another twig from an old nest that was being repaired. He took two more from a new nest and three from one that was quite finished. He was very artful – he always waited until the owners of the nest had flown away for more twigs before he stole any.

Soon his nest was finished, and he cawed loudly to the other young rooks, telling them that his nest was the first new one to be built – but they did not caw back. No – they all wondered how it was that their best twigs had been stolen! They flew to Caw-caw's nest and had a look at it. 'Caw!' cried a rook and pulled out a twig. 'This is *my* twig!' And he flew off with it. 'Caw!' cried another, '*I* found this twig, and you must have taken it.' He pulled it out and flew with it to his nest. Soon there was nothing at all left of Caw-caw's beautifully built nest, and he was sad and angry, for a lovely lady rook had promised to marry him as soon as his nest was built – and now she had gone off with another rook!

'It serves you right!' said the old rooks who had been watching. 'We'll see that such a thing doesn't happen again!'

And what do you think they do now? You can see them any day in the springtime building their nests – *but they always leave one rook guarding each nest when they leave it to go hunting for twigs!*

The Bad Sixpenny-Bit

SLY-ONE found the bad sixpenny-bit in the buttercup field. 'Ho!' he said, 'here's a sixpence, but it's a bad one. Never mind, I'll give it to some one, and they won't know.'

He went to Timmy Mouse and bought a big piece of cheese from him. 'Here's sixpence for it,' he said to Timmy, and gave him the bad sixpence. Timmy put it into his purse without looking at it.

Timmy Mouse put on his hat and went to buy a new walking-stick from Skippitty the pixie. He chose one with a nice crooked handle. 'Here's sixpence for it,' he said, and gave Skippitty the bad sixpenny-bit. Skippitty put it into his pocket without looking at it.

Then Skippitty the pixie took his shopping basket and went to buy a string of onions from Mother Patchy over the way. 'They're sixpence a string,' she said, so Skippitty took the onions and paid her the bad sixpence. She was short-sighted so she didn't see that it wasn't a good one.

That afternoon Mother Patchy saw a poor old beggarman standing outside Mr Biscuit the baker's, looking into the window. She was sorry for him, and she gave him the bad sixpence thinking it was a good one. 'Go and buy yourself three jam-tarts,' she said.

The beggarman thanked her and ran inside the shop. He bought three big jam-tarts and gave Mr Biscuit the bad sixpence. The baker popped it inside his till not guessing that it was a bad one. Presently his little girl came in and asked him for some money to buy a doll.

'Here is sixpence,' said Mr Biscuit, and gave her the bad sixpenny-bit. She ran off to Dame Dinky, who sold lovely dolls, and looked in at the window.

Then she went into the shop and asked Dame Dinky to sell her a little baby doll with blue eyes and dark hair. 'It is sixpence,' said Dame Dinky, wrapping up the doll. The little girl gave her the bad sixpenny-bit and ran home.

'I do feel as if I'd like some nice apples,' said Dame Dinky to herself. 'I think I'll pop over to Sly-One's and ask him if he can sell me a few of the lovely red apples he picked from his big apple-tree this year.'

She put on her bonnet and shawl and ran over

to Sly-One's cottage. 'Can you sell me some apples?' she asked. 'Yes,' said Sly-One. 'They are sixpence a basket.'

'I'll have a basketful,' said Dame Dinky. 'Here's a sixpence.' She gave him the sixpenny-bit and he popped it into his pocket without looking at it. Dame Dinky said good afternoon and trotted back home.

'I think I'll go and buy myself a big bag of peppermint creams,' said Sly-One. So he put on his pointed cap and went to Mrs Sugary, who kept the village sweet-shop. But when he took out the sixpence to pay her he found that it was a bad one!

'Oh!' he cried in a rage. 'Dame Dinky's given me a bad sixpenny-bit! I'll fetch the policeman and have her locked up!' So off he went to Mr Burly the policeman and banged loudly at his door.

Mr Burly, the policeman, heard Sly-One knocking and came to the door. 'Look here!' said Sly-One, holding up the bad sixpenny-bit. 'Here's a bad sixpence, given to me by that wicked Dame Dinky.'

'Dear, dear!' said Mr Burly. 'We must go and see her about it.' So off they went and knocked at Dame Dinky's cottage door. When she heard what they had come about she was dreadfully upset.

'Why, Mr Biscuit's little girl gave it to me,' she said.

'Well, we'll go to the baker's and see what *he* has to say,' said Mr Burly. So off they all went and walked into Mr Biscuit's shop. 'Your little girl gave Dame Dinky a bad sixpenny-bit,' said Mr Burly to the surprised baker.

'Well, I never!' said Mr Biscuit, looking quite worried. 'I gave it to her out of the till. Let me see – who gave it to me? Oh, it was the old beggarman! Look, there he is asleep by the hedge.'

'We'll go and ask him about it,' said Mr Burly the policeman. So they all went over to the beggarman and woke him up. He was frightened when he saw Mr Burly. 'Where did you get that sixpence from that you bought the jam-tarts with?' asked Mr Burly.

'M-m-m-mother P-p-p-patchy gave it to m-m-m-me!' he stammered. 'Oh, I really didn't know it was a bad one!'

'Well, we'll go and ask Mother Patchy about it,' said Mr Burly. 'You can come along too, beggarman.' So they all went to Mother Patchy's, and asked her where *she* got the bad sixpence. 'Skippitty the pixie gave it to me,' she said. 'He bought a string of onions for sixpence.'

'Well, we'll go and see Skippitty the pixie,' said Mr Burly. And off they all went, quite a crowd of them by this time. Skippitty was digging in his garden and he wondered what they wanted. Mr Burly soon told him. 'Was that sixpence really a bad one,' said Skippitty. 'I got it from Timmy Mouse. He bought a walking-stick with a crooked handle.'

'Well, we'll all go and see Timmy Mouse,' said Mr Burly. So off they went again, and soon came to Timmy Mouse's house. His nose woffled with fright when he heard about it. '*I* didn't know it was bad,' he said.

'Who gave it to you?' asked Mr Burly. Timmy Mouse looked around – and then he pointed to Sly-One, who was looking very much afraid. 'Why, *he* gave it to me when he came to buy some cheese!' he said.

'*What*!' cried every one. 'Why, it was Sly-One who went to complain to Mr Burly, and tried to get poor old Mother Dinky put into prison.'

'Where did *you* get it from?' asked Mr Burly, sternly, and Sly-One shivered in his pointed shoes.

'I f-f-f-found it in the b-b-b-buttercup f-f-field!' he said, hanging his head.

'Where's that walking-stick. Timmy bought?' said Mr Burly, looking round. Timmy gave it to him – and, oh, my, what a beating Sly-One got! He ran down the street crying big tears, and as far as *I* know he never, never tried to give any one a bad sixpenny-bit again!

Hot Roast Chestnuts

NODDY the gnome had a barrow that he wheeled down the streets of Fairyland in the winter-time, calling 'Hot Roast Chestnuts!' all the time. On his barrow was a little stove that roasted the chestnuts, and by the side of it lay hundreds of unroasted ones. Noddy did a roaring trade, for the gnomes, pixies and brownies were very fond of roast chestnuts.

'I want some one to help me,' said Noddy, at the beginning of the winter. So he went to Prickles the Hedgehog.

'Will you push my barrow for me?' he asked.

'No, thank you,' said Prickles. 'Don't you know that I curl myself up in the dead leaves that lie in the ditch and snore all winter through?'

Then Noddy went to Big-Eyes the Frog.

'Will you push my barrow for me?' he asked.

'No, thank you,' said Big-Eyes. 'Don't you know that I stand on my head in the mud at the bottom of the pond all winter through?'

Then Noddy went to Sleeky the Grass-Snake.

'Will you push my barrow for me?' he asked.

'No, thank you,' said Sleeky. 'Don't you know that I and my brothers sleep in a tangled knot under the pile of brushwood all winter through?'

Then Noddy sighed heavily and wondered whom to ask next. He went to Curly-Shell, the biggest snail in the garden.

'Will you push my barrow for me?' he asked.

'No, thank you,' said Curly-Shell. 'Don't you know that I grow a hard little door over the opening to my shell, and sleep under a stone on the rockery all winter through?'

Then Noddy was quite in despair and didn't know *what* to do. He saw Peek-about the Tortoise and ran up to him.

'Will *you* push my barrow for me?' he asked.

'No, thank you,' said Peek-about. 'Don't you know that I dig a hole in the ground and bury myself all winter through?'

Just then Dozy the Dormouse ran by, and Noddy scampered after him.

'Will you push my barrow for me?' he asked.

'No, thank you,' said Dozy. 'Don't you know that I find a nice warm hole in a bank and sleep soundly all winter through?'

Noddy went out into the middle of a grassy field and wept loudly.

'Everybody sleeps in the winter-time, and there's no one to push my barrow for me!' he sobbed.

Up popped a rabbit's head out of a hole.

'*I* don't sleep all the winter through!' he said. 'Let *me* push your barrow for you, and for payment you shall give me six big chestnuts to gnaw.'

So Noddy joyfully took the rabbit to help him, and together they go down the streets of Fairyland crying, 'Hot Roast Chestnuts! Hot Roast Chestnuts! Buy! Buy! Buy!'

I'd love to see them, wouldn't you?

Brer Rabbit Again

ONCE Brer Rabbit found that he had quite a lot of money in his purse, and when his old woman heard it jingling-jangling she spoke up loudly.

'Hey, Brer Rabbit,' she said. 'You're rich! You go off to market and buy a large coffee-pot for us, and seven tin mugs and plates for the children.'

'I will,' said Brer Rabbit. 'I'll go next market-day, sure as rabbits have whiskers!'

Well, old Mrs Rabbit was so delighted to hear that, that she ran off to Mrs Bear and told her how generous Brer Rabbit was to his family. Old Mrs Bear told Brer Bear *he* ought to be generous too, and she grumbled at him all night long. Then she went to Mrs Fox and told her what Mrs Rabbit had said, and Mrs Fox scolded Brer Fox.

Then Mrs Fox told Mrs Mink, and Mrs Mink talked and talked to her husband about it till he was so tired of it he went to call on Brer Fox and Brer Bear to see what they thought.

'Hoo!' said Brer Bear, in a very bad temper. 'I'm just about tired of hearing what a wonderful fellow Brer Rabbit is. What about lying in wait for him next market day, and taking away the things he's buying for his family? Then he'll have to go home without them!'

So on market-day they all lay in wait for Brer Rabbit. Pretty soon he came along with his goods, and sat down under a black-jack tree for a rest. And he hadn't been there long before he saw marks in the sand in front of him.

'Ho!' said Brer Rabbit, looking closely. 'Here's where Brer Fox sat and there's the mark of his bushy tail. And here's where Brer Bear sat and there's the mark where his tail wasn't. And here's where old Brer Mink sat – and I guess they're all lying in wait for me in the gully a bit farther along!'

Then old Brer Rabbit, he grinned to himself and did a little dance. Then he took his large coffee-pot and stuck it upside down on his head. He strung the seven tin mugs on a string through their handles and hung them down his back. He took the seven tin plates in his hands, and then crept to the top of the gully. Sure enough, there were Brer Bear, Brer Mink and Brer Fox. Brer Bear was asleep, but Brer Fox and Brer Mink were wide awake.

Brer Rabbit suddenly tore down the hill into the gully clashing the tin plates with all his might, his tin mugs clattering behind him.

'Ho, ho, ho!' he yelled. 'Here I come, I'm the Spewter-Splutter Man, I'm snaggle-toothed and double-jointed, I've claws in my hands and scales down my back! Ho, ho, ho!'

Well, Brer Bear woke up with a dreadful start, and when he saw Brer Rabbit with the coffee-pot on his head, making such a terrible noise, he gave a roar and ran for his life. He tripped over Brer Fox and sent Brer Mink into a bed of nettles, and all the time Brer Rabbit shouted and clanked behind them. What a scare they got!

As for old Brer Rabbit, he laughed till the coffee-pot fell off his head!

The Sugar Stork

ONCE upon a time Cook made a beautiful cake for Gillian Mary's christening, and on the top of it she put a lovely white stork made of sugar. The stork stood on two long legs, and in his long beak he held a tiny cradle with a baby doll in it.

Now when the cake was all eaten the stork had nothing to stand on, and he was afraid he might be eaten too, like the cake. So what did he do but put down the little cradle and hop off the plate, helping himself with his sugar wings.

'Stop! Stop!' cried Gillian's Nanny. 'You are for Gillian Mary! Come back!' But the sugar stork took not a bit of notice and ran out of the door.

He hurried out into the garden, and the first person he met was Pat the cat.

'Stop! Stop!' she cried. 'You are for Gillian Mary! Come back!' But the sugar stork took not a bit of notice, and ran on down the garden.

Soon he met Thomasina, the slow old tortoise, and danced round him on his spindly legs, making a queer, sugary kind of noise. Then off he went again.

'Stop! Stop!' cried Thomasina, 'you are for Gillian Mary! Come back!' But the stork took not a bit of notice, and danced on out into the lane. Near by, looking over the hedge, were Darling and Blossom, the two big horses. They thought the stork would make a nice mouthful, for they were both fond of a bit of sugar, so they called to him with a neigh.

'Stop! Stop!' they cried. 'You are for Gillian Mary! Come back!' But the stork took not a bit of notice and went running on. Presently Bimbo, the other cat, saw him, and came running after him in surprise, for he had never seen a bird quite like that before. But when he knew that it was the christening stork he shouted after him loudly.

'Stop! Stop! You are for Gillian Mary! Come back!' But the stork took not a bit of notice, and went racing on with Bimbo after him.

Now Bimbo could run very fast, and the sugar stork began to be afraid that he would be caught. He looked about for a hiding-place, and saw a little yard not far away enclosed all round by wire netting. He slipped in through the wire and stood in the yard panting for breath.

There was a kennel in the yard, and out of it looked two dogs, Sandy and Bobs. When they saw the sugar stork they were most excited.

'It's cold out there,' said Sandy. 'Come in here.'

'It's windy out there,' said Bobs. 'Come in here.'

'If you want to hide there is plenty of straw here,' said Sandy.

'If you'd like to sleep, it's very comfortable in here,' said Bobs.

So the foolish sugar stork went into the kennel – and in a trice he had disappeared!

'What a beautiful stork that was!' said Bobs, licking his lips.

'Well, he's gone to a good home!' said Sandy, and ran off to tell cook!

The Toadstool Frills

THE Queen of Fairyland was going to give a very grand party, because the Prince of Heyho was coming to visit her. She called for her cooks, her needlewomen and her musicians, and told them all to do their best to make her party a great success.

The cooks set to work to make puddings and jellies, cakes and sandwiches, lemonade and honey drinks. The needlewomen began to make a beautiful dress for the Queen, a new cloak for the King, and soft cushions to put on the toadstools that were grown in a fairy ring for seats. The musicians, a little band of pixies with a rabbit for conductor, practised their dance tunes all day long.

Now there was a little elf called Nimble-Thimble who could sew beautifully, and she longed to help the Queen. So she went to the needlewomen and begged them to let her make frills for a cushion.

'No,' they said, 'we shall do it all ourselves. It

is conceited of you to think you can sew well enough to make cushions for the Queen.'

Then Nimble-Thimble went to the cooks, and asked them if they would let her make frills to put round the pudding dishes. But they wouldn't hear of it.

'Don't come interfering with us!' they said. 'You are very vain to think you can sew well enough to make frills for our puddings!'

Then Nimble-Thimble went to the musicians and begged them to let her make a neat frill round the platform they stood on. But they laughed at her and sent her away.

Nimble-Thimble was very sad, and ran away by herself. But she so badly wanted to sew something for the Queen, that she made up her mind to use her clever needle somehow. So that night she crept to where the toadstools stood in a silent ring, waiting for the dance evening to come, and looked around her.

'I don't see *anything* I can do!' she sighed. Then a queer idea came to her, and she ran to a toadstool and looked underneath its big round top.

'I'll sew hundreds of little fine frills underneath!' she thought, joyfully. 'Nobody will see them, but they will be there, and I shall have done something for the dear Queen after all!'

So, very quickly, she began to sew tiny frills underneath each toadstool, and when dawn came, they were all finished, and Nimble-Thimble crept away.

That night, when the dance had begun, and the pixie band was playing merrily, the Prince of Heyho sat down on a toadstool that was too small for him. It broke, and over he went with a bump. Every one ran to help him, and soon he was on his feet again, laughing merrily.

Suddenly he looked at the fallen toadstool and noticed the beautiful frills.

'Who has sewn these?' he cried. 'What wonderful work to hide!'

Then Nimble-Thimble was fetched, for every one guessed it was she who had sewn the frills, and what a lovely time she had! She danced three times with the Prince of Heyho, and ate seven ices.

As for her beautiful frills, you can see them any day. Just turn up a toadstool and have a look at them.

The Vain Fox

ONCE upon a time a fox found an old hat in a ditch. He put it on his head, and at once thought that he must look very grand indeed.

'I am now crowned!' he said to himself. 'I am a king! I will be lord of all the animals in the wood!'

Then he built himself a platform of twigs just by a pool where the animals of the wood used to come and drink, and called it his throne. He sat there one night, wearing the old hat and looking very high and mighty indeed.

Soon a hare came by to drink, and the fox shouted to him:

'Hare! You must not drink until you have repeated this rhyme to me:

He sits on a throne, he wears a fine crown,
His servant am I, and I shake at his frown!'

The hare was thirsty, and thought the fox was playing a joke on him. He quickly said the rhyme, and then drank. Soon there came a hedgehog, and the fox called to him too:

'Hedgehog! You must not drink until you have said the rhyme to me.'

The hedgehog mumbled the words over and then drank, wondering why the fox should make such a silly joke. Then he ran off. Other animals came to drink, and the fox made them all say the rhyme.

The fox became vainer than ever. He sat up very straight and called haughtily to the weasel, when he also came to drink.

'Weasel! You must not drink until you have said this rhyme to me:

He sits on a throne, he wears a fine crown,
His servant am I, and I shake at his frown.'

'Oh, just let me have a drink first, for my throat is too dry to repeat your words properly,' said the weasel.

'Very well,' said the fox.

The weasel grinned to himself and took a long drink. Then he began to edge away from the fox, for *he* did not mean to repeat such a foolish rhyme.

'Hie!' cried the fox. 'Come here! You haven't said my rhyme.'

'Dear me, I almost forgot,' said the weasel, getting a little farther away. 'Let me see, how did it go?'

'He sits on a throne – ' said the fox.

'Ah, yes!' said the weasel, edging away still farther. 'I can say it!

> 'He sits on the twigs, an old hat on his ears,
> But, oh, does he know what a *goose* he appears!'

With that the cheeky weasel tore off as fast as he could. The fox listened in anger and amazement, and then he raced after the weasel like the wind.

The weasel popped straight into a rabbit-hole, but the fox caught him by the tail – and how he pulled! The weasel pulled one way and the fox another – and at last the weasel cried:

'Oh, my tail is breaking! Let go, fox, and I will turn round and come out to you.'

So the fox let go, and, of course, the weasel scampered down the hole and disappeared in a twinkling!

Pixie Sandals

ON the night of the full moon the Golden Pixies dance in the fields, on the commons and in the woods. There are hundreds of them, all dressed in golden tunics, and their hair is shining gold, too.

On their feet they wear the tiniest golden-brown sandals you can imagine. These are made by the Wise Woman on Tip-top Hill, and have to last exactly a year, for they are very finely made and expensive to buy.

The pixies don't wear their sandals at all except on dance nights, and all the time between they hide them away carefully. For years and years they hid them under the leaves of the daisies in the fields, and they were quite safe there, for if you look at a daisy plant you will see that the leaves lie flat to the ground and hide anything underneath.

Then there came a dreadful night, when the moon rose silvery and round, and the Golden Pixies found that their little dance-sandals were gone! Someone had stolen them!

'But who can have taken them?' asked a pixie in despair. 'Why, there are hundreds and hundreds gone! If one pair had been taken, or perhaps half-a-dozen, it wouldn't have been so bad; but quite 500 are gone, and we can't dance any more till the year is up and the Wise Woman makes us some new sandals.'

Well, who do you think had taken them? Ten long centipedes! You know them – don't you? – long, quick-running creatures with a hundred legs each. One centipede had discovered the sandals under the daisies, and he had taken fifty pairs to his hundred feet. Then he had called the rest of his family, and they had taken hundreds more of the little golden-brown sandals. How proud they were of them!

They wouldn't give them back, and the Golden Pixies grew pale and sad when each full-moon night came and they could not dance. Not until the New Year dawned, and the Wise Woman sent them hundreds of new pairs of sandals did they smile again and skip about merrily.

'But where shall we hide them this time?' they wondered. 'The centipedes are sure to find them if we put them under the daisy leaves again.'

'Tuck them into the dandelion flowers,' said one. 'No, the centipedes will find them there,' said another. 'Well, *I* know,' cried a third. 'We'll hide them in the stinging-nettles, and then no one will go near them for fear of being stung!'

'But, you silly, *we* shall get stung, too, if we have to go into the nettles each month to find our shoes!' cried all the other pixies. '*That* won't do!'

And then Skippitty, the tiniest pixie of all, had a wonderful idea.

'Let's hide them in the flowers of the white dead-nettle!' she cried. 'The dead-nettles *look* like stinging-nettles, so the centipedes will keep away from them – but they won't sting us when we go to find our shoes!'

Well, the pixies put their sandals there – tucked carefully inside the top lip of the white dead-nettle flower. How do I know? Because I've seen them there, heaps of times! Would you like to see them too? Well, find a white dead-nettle and look into the top lip of each flower.

As sure as anything you will find four tiny golden-brown sandals there, in two neat pairs. Just look and see!

'Pink-Pink!'

ONCE upon a time the Princess Tiptoes decided to give a party. So she wrote out the invitations to all the brownies, gnomes, pixies, and elves, and this is what she said:

'Please come to my party
on the night of the
next full moon.
Prizes will be given to
the one who comes dressed
in a secret colour I
have chosen.
With love from Princess Tiptoes.'

Well, these invitations *did* make every one excited. To begin with, a party was lively anyhow, but a party with prizes!

'I do wonder what the secret colour is,' said a pixie. 'It might be harebell blue. I shall make my dress that colour.'

'*I* think it might be robin-red,' said a gnome.

'I know the Princess is fond of robins. *I* shall make my tunic *that* colour.'

'Well, the Princess simply loves the yellow crocuses, because I heard her say so the other day,' said an elf. 'My frock shall be *that* colour!'

Now the Princess had already chosen the colour that should win the prize at the party. It was pale pink, the colour of almond blossom. One morning she sat down and wrote on a piece of paper, and this is what she wrote: 'The secret colour I have chosen is almond blossom pink.' Then she put the paper in an envelope, sealed it up, and put it away safely until the night of the party.

'Nobody knows what I have chosen except myself,' she said . 'It will be fun to see if any one comes dressed in almond-blossom pink!'

But someone else *did* know the colour she had chosen – and that was the little chaffinch who had perched on the window-sill whilst she was writing her letter. He had peeped over her shoulder and read what she had written.

And could he keep a secret? No, not he! He at once flew away and shouted all over the place: 'Pink! Pink-pink! Pink!'

Well, the elfin folk couldn't help hearing him, and do you know what they did? Why, every one of them began to make a dress of palest pink, for they all remembered the lovely almond blossom tree that was in flower in the garden belonging to the Princess!

And on the night of the party – oh, dear me! *How* astonished the Princess was! Every single guest was dressed in pink! Whatever should she do about the prizes? She only had three, and *they* wouldn't go far among so many. Quickly she got out her purse and sent her maid to buy enough for every one – but it *did* make her poor!

'Who told my secret?' she asked, crossly. 'My party is all spoilt!'

'The chaffinch told, the chaffinch told!' cried every one. So he was fetched and well spanked, and wasn't he sorry for himself!

But the funny thing is that he couldn't stop saying, 'Pink-pink!' Do listen for him, and you'll hear him saying it now, very loud and clear. 'Pink-pink!' he says. Isn't it strange?

Brer Rabbit and Mister Lion

IT happened one morning when Brer Rabbit was strolling through the woods that a bit of a wind began to blow. Brer Rabbit was afraid perhaps a tree would be blown down, so he took to his heels and began to run lippitty-clippitty through the wood.

By and by he bumped right into Mr Lion.

'What's the hurry?' asked Mr Lion.

'Run, Mr Lion, run!' said Brer Rabbit. 'There's a hurricane a-getting up! You'd better run!'

That made Mr Lion rather scared.

'I'm a bit too heavy to run, Brer Rabbit,' he said. 'What shall I do?'

'Lie down, Mr Lion, lie down! Get close to the ground, then you won't be blown over.'

Mr Lion shook his head. 'If the wind can blow a little fellow like you along, what will it do to a big fellow like me? It will surely blow me to the end of the world!'

'Well, hug a tree, hug a tree!' said Brer Rabbit.

'Yes, but suppose the wind blows all day and all night, Brer Rabbit! I can't hug a tree all that time, I'd be tired out.'

'Well, let me tie you to the tree, Mr Lion,' said Brer Rabbit. 'Let me tie you to the tree!'

Mr Lion agreed to this, so Brer Rabbit got a rope and tied him fast to a tree. Then Brer Rabbit sat himself down and began to wash his hands and face just like a cat does.

'Why don't you go running?' asked Mr Lion in surprise.

'Oh, I think I'll stay here and take care of you, Mr Lion,' said Brer Rabbit.

'I don't seem to hear any hurricane,' said Mr Lion after a bit. 'Nor do I,' said Brer Rabbit.

'I can't even hear any wind a-blowing,' said Mr Lion. 'Nor can I,' said Brer Rabbit, still washing himself.

'There doesn't seem to be so much as a leaf a-stirring,' said Mr Lion. 'Nor is there!' said Brer Rabbit. 'They're all as still as still!'

'Well, you unloose me then,' said Mr Lion, in a temper. 'You unloose me, Brer Rabbit.'

'I'm afraid to,' said Brer Rabbit.

Then Mr Lion knew Brer Rabbit had played a trick on him and he was mighty wild. He began to roar and bellow so loudly that all the other animals came running up to see what the matter was.

'What's Mr Lion tied up for?' they said. 'And who tied him up?'

'I did,' said Brer Rabbit, looking as proud as two cock-sparrows. 'Mr Lion offended me, so I took him and tied him up, and there he is! And you be careful, all you others, in case I tie *you* up too!'

And with that he stalked away by himself and left the animals staring after him in fear and astonishment. Oh, Brer Rabbit was a mighty clever creature!

Hey Diddle-Diddle

DO you know the story of Hey Diddle-Diddle? Well, if you don't I must tell it to you.

There was once a cat who was very fond of music. She went to a music master, and he taught her how to play the fiddle. Oh, but she could play the liveliest tunes. Jig-a-jig-jig, and rumpatidee, and tiddley-um-tum, and all the rest of them. Once you heard them you couldn't keep still. Your feet jigged up and down, and you *had* to dance.

Now, once on her travels the cat met a cow that couldn't walk. It was in a wheelbarrow, and a little dog wheeled the cow along, and sighed and sorrowed with the weight of his big friend.

Behind the dog walked a dish and a spoon. They had to walk because the little dog wouldn't carry any more in the wheelbarrow. They were a very sorry lot, for the cow groaned, the dog sighed and sorrowed, and the dish and the spoon grumbled because they had to walk so many miles in a day.

'Where are you going?' asked the cat with the fiddle, when she met them.

'I am trying to find a doctor to cure the cow's legs,' said the little dog, sobbing. 'She cannot walk, and the weight of her is very heavy.'

'I will go with you,' said the cat. So they all journeyed on together, the dog wheeling the cow, the cat walking beside them, and the dish and the spoon lagging behind.

Now when they lay down to rest for the night the moon came up, and the cat began to feel jolly. She took her fiddle and said she would play her friends a tune. So out came all the tunes she knew – jig-a-jig-jig, rumpatidee, tiddley-um-tum, and all the rest of them.

Well, as soon as the cow heard the music she felt such a tickling in her legs that she had to get up. Then her feet began to caper all about, and there was the old cow dancing like mad! The little dog sat up and gaped at her. Then he forgot his sorrows and began to laugh. How he laughed! It was ha ha ha! and he he he! and ho ho ho! and a dozen other laughs besides. The cow kicked up her heels and whisked her tail – and suddenly she saw the moon!

With a mighty leap she jumped right over it, and the moon gave a wobble of fright. The dog laughed till he cried – but the dish and the spoon were frightened and they took to their heels and ran far away.

'Oh, cat with the fiddle!' cried the dog. 'You are a marvel! You have made the cow quite better! How happy I am! Now stop your fiddling and let us sleep.'

In the morning the cow went to a farmer. The dog found a good master. The dish and the spoon were caught by a tramp, and he put them in his bag and used them at breakfast, dinner and tea. But what about the cat and the fiddle?

Ah, they went off towards the rising sun, and nobody has heard of them from that day to this!